This revelatory, moving and ingeniously structured book will make readers think and become readier to talk about cancer, a subject that is, for many, still wrapped in siler
whose life has been affected by the c
– a book, in other words, for everyone

Kate Kellaway, The Observer critic

G000057218

Helena's book is an inspiring and las
who has gone through a devastating cancer diagnosis and offers a powerful collection of stories and experiences. We are honoured to be part of this uniquely unifying project.

Sarah Lindsell, The Brain Tumour Charity

An incredible initiative. Opening up the conversation about cancer is just one way we can normalise discussion and help those affected feel free to speak out. Books like this are so important in connecting people through shared experiences.

@phoebe_geary on twitter

ISBN 978-1-9162965-1-0

Designed by Helena Traill
hello@helenatraill.co.uk
helenatraill.co.uk

Typeset in Space Grotesk 11pt
A font by Florian Karsten

Printing and binding by Ripping Image Ltd
Printed in Great Britain 2019

This book is not intended as a substitute for medical advice.
All the views expressed are personal to the storyteller.

Want to find out more? Follow along @100StoriesBook

With grateful thanks for the help and support

Let's make every journey with cancer, a little bit
easier. Founder James McNaught took inspiration
from the TFL Baby On Board badge whilst he was
undergoing treatment – treatment that left him
exhausted, weak and gradually, unable to speak.
And so the Cancer On Board badge was born.
canceronboard.org

The world's leading brain tumour charity and the
largest dedicated funder of research into brain
tumours globally to increase survival and improve
treatment options. As well as raising awareness of
the symptoms and effects of brain tumours to bring
about earlier diagnosis, they also provide support
for everyone affected so that they can live as full
a life as possible, with the best quality of life.
thebraintumourcharity.org

Maggie's helps anyone affected by cancer.
At Maggie's you can talk to and get support from a
range of professionals. Our 22 centres are staffed
by Cancer Support Specialists, Benefits Advisors,
Nutritionists, Therapists and Psychologists, all
providing support in whichever way best suits you.
maggiescentres.org

100 Stories

For the storytellers who trusted me with their stories, Nell Wood, Rebecca Gwyther and my parents, Philip and Angela Traill

James McNaught
Founder of Cancer On Board

100 Stories encourages and enables cancer patients to talk. It can be easy to forget that each patient is not a statistic but an individual. In the voices of the patients themselves, these stories show how different the experience of cancer can be for each person and that there is no such thing as average. We are delighted to be involved with this important project and that Helena has chosen to use our logo in its creation.

Cancer On Board was born out of the need for cancer patients to make themselves known on public transport. The majority of us look completely 'normal', yet the idea that cancer can be a hidden disability remains a novel one to many people.

Our 'Cancer On Board' badges nudge commuters to look out for the previously hidden cancer patients amongst them. These patients might need to sit down or get to the front of a queue, but might lack the confidence – or the energy – to make a fuss. The badges also encourage open conversation about what, to many, is still a taboo subject. By showing that cancer patients are 'just like you and me', we can break down the stigma and lessen the fear.

Lucy Shaverin
Stories Manager for Maggie's

Cancer is all too often a subject that is not talked about. But as Stories Manager at Maggie's, I have seen how important the sharing and exchanging of stories is for people with cancer, and their families. When we share our own or hear another's story, we are reminded that there are others going through a similar experience at a time that can be isolating and scary. Knowing you are not alone can help.

At Maggie's, stories are at the heart of everything we do. Whether people with cancer are sharing their stories around the kitchen table in each of our centres, on social media, at talks or through the Press and TV, they bring people together, break down stigmas, and build communities. That's what Maggie's is about.

I feel very privileged to be able to work with Maggie's Centre visitors, helping them to tell their stories in a way that feels most comfortable to them. I am always amazed by how much courage people show in talking candidly about what they are going through (be that a person with cancer, a family member, friend or carer).

When I first met Helena in Maggie's West London to talk about her book, I felt straight away that we should be working together. I was so impressed with how Helena's ideas have led to a collection of portraits and stories. Sharing your cancer story requires strength, bravery and a leap of faith. It is a testament to Helena that so many people have opened up to her so honestly. Her book gives a voice to people with cancer in such a creative way. Differing accounts show that cancer does not discriminate and that each person is so much more than their illness. It even, at times, reveals the unexpected positivity found in a cancer diagnosis.

Helena is kindly giving one book to every Maggie's centre. I know some of our visitors will pick up this book and, as they browse, find a story that resonates at a time when they need it most. I know it will spark conversations around many a Maggie's kitchen table across the country and am so excited to see what it will do.

Introduction
Helena Traill

Never did I think I would actually need to re-write my dissertation for an introduction of a book. So to start off with: wow, this is crazy! Thank you to every single backer of my Kickstarter campaign, who has made this dream a reality, and to every storyteller (including the ones who aren't in the 100 stories). Thank you for taking the time to write out your story and share it with all the eyes that will see this book.

For those of you who don't know, this project started towards the end of my Graphic Communication Design degree at Central Saint Martins in January 2019. But these ideas started before then, so let me explain my story.

After studying A-level Fine Art, Photography and Textiles, I went on to an Art Foundation at Central Saint Martins. I ticked the wrong box on the application form so ended up on the Graphic Design pathway (a happy mistake). It turned out that Graphic Design was perfect for me – it mixed all the things I love doing: image making and storytelling.

At the time, I was having panic attacks in the night after seeing my father have epileptic fits – my father has two cancerous brain tumours which cause his epilepsy. So for one of the modules I created a film about epilepsy, I tried to tackle the scary monster head on and visualise it through my art. It turned out that the decision to scrutinise was powerful and that it was better for my mental health than all six of my previous counsellors. It was cathartic and self-healing. Then a few years later (by this time studying on the degree course at Central Saint Martins), I found myself creating a similar animation, but about Attention Deficit Hyperactive Disorder (ADHD). I was diagnosed with ADHD a few years previously and always found it fascinating that when I told people about it, they wouldn't believe me. The majority said, 'But you're not hyperactive'. By contrast, my boyfriend, Bernard, had been told his whole life by friends, 'Oh you are so ADHD, you can't sit still' – but he was not diagnosed until recently. So I animated this difference and, to my amazement, it helped a few people.

That's when it clicked; what if, through my art, I could break down stigmas by telling stories in an honest way? A few weeks later I decided to base my final major project on the 'Big-C'.

Creating 100 Stories of Cancer

My initial research looked at cancer stories in the public eye. I thought that many adverts/films/articles were not presented in an honest way. So my aim was to tell cancer stories and spark open discussion. Then I needed my own stories to tell.

I reached out to a family friend, Vix (story number 99). In our initial interview, Vix told me about the charity Cancer On Board. And what a great idea the charity is: a small item, a badge, that encourages open conversation amongst commuters. Wearers are often approached to ask why they wear it and what it means. This was especially the case for Vix, because she never lost her hair and still wore badass heels to work in central London in between her chemotherapy cycles. A few weeks later, I met James, the founder of Cancer On Board and he told me his story. I asked if I could use his badge and symbol as part of my project.

I created social media accounts (originally @TheCancerChapter, now @100StoriesBook) and James helped me spread the word to collect stories and make portraits. James was my main ally – he knew the power of #CancerTwitter (as he likes to call it) and I didn't. So to my surprise, within a month or so, I had conducted 15 face-to-face interviews, emailed over 200 people and made 123 portraits. I was surprised by the sheer number of stories and moved by the trust people showed in talking to me. They had no idea what I was going to create.

From the filmed interviews, I had 5 hours 38 minutes and 17 seconds of footage – way too much. I spent days listening back to each interview and trying to make a storyline out of the dialogue. The topics covered included: people who 'get it', people who don't get it, children's reactions, community, diagnosis, doctors' language, emotions, normalising the conversation, open conversation, remission, social media, side-effects and preconceptions. We also discussed the struggle to arrive at a clear picture of cancer because it comes in so many different forms (over 200), so, for many people, the all important question is: 'What does cancer look like?'. As you can see, it was impossible to make this into a single storyline and then animate it (it would have to be the length of a blockbuster film). So I decided instead to animate just one story: Martino Sclavi.

This was the story that resonated with my own the most. Martino is a film director and, in 2011, was diagnosed with grade four glioblastoma – an aggressive form of brain tumour. He underwent surgery immediately in LA, soon after the diagnosis and then had a second operation back home in Rome six months later. The second surgery initially left him unable to speak, read or write. Martino relearnt his three languages and started to use technology to read text out for him. Before I met him, I found it hard to believe he couldn't actually read. But when I went to visit him, he produced eight packets of tea and asked me to identify which of them was English Breakfast.

He is still unable to read but managed to write an entire book about his story through touch typing. What is remarkable is that his muscle memory remembered how to touch type. His book, The Finch In My Brain, explains his life before and after being diagnosed with a brain tumour. My favourite part is where he explains that, when he looked at the hole in his brain, he saw a bird, a finch, and from then onwards, he created a relationship with the bird. I cannot recommend his book enough (and if you are a Russell Brand fan, you might be interested in reading about Martino's friendship with him).

I am extremely grateful to Piers Townley at The Brain Tumour Charity for introducing me to Martino. And to Martino, who welcomed me into his home for an interview and has continued to inspire my work ever since. He was the first person I have met who has similar mannerisms to my father. These things include subtle movements and an emphasis on certain words, things that others might not notice. However for me, this was quite bizarre and touching.

Now, skipping forward a few months, I had finished the book and the animation (which included hand painting roughly 300 frames) and it was displayed at the Central Saint Martins degree show. All the storytellers were invited to the show and I was delighted to see about twenty of them throughout the week. A lot of them asked when they would be able to read all the stories and one lady even sat down and read 52 stories in one go. So I knew I wanted to continue with the project and here we are.

The book contains 100 portraits, digitalised using the Cancer On Board symbol. You may notice that as you progress through the book the portraits get clearer. This clarity is in correlation with the amount each person says, e.g. the more words the more detailed the image.

My father is story number one in the book, because initially he didn't want to tell his story. He does not like talking about his brain tumours, because he doesn't want to come across as compromised or ill. However to my amazement, 24 hours before I sent this book to print, he wrote a few sentences to put alongside his portrait. I said when I started this project that if this gets my dad talking about his illness, then it will be all be worth it.

This is how I ended up with a 462 page book. A book, which I hope, can help many people. And maybe it actually contains 101 stories – because one of them is mine.

100 Stories

Philip

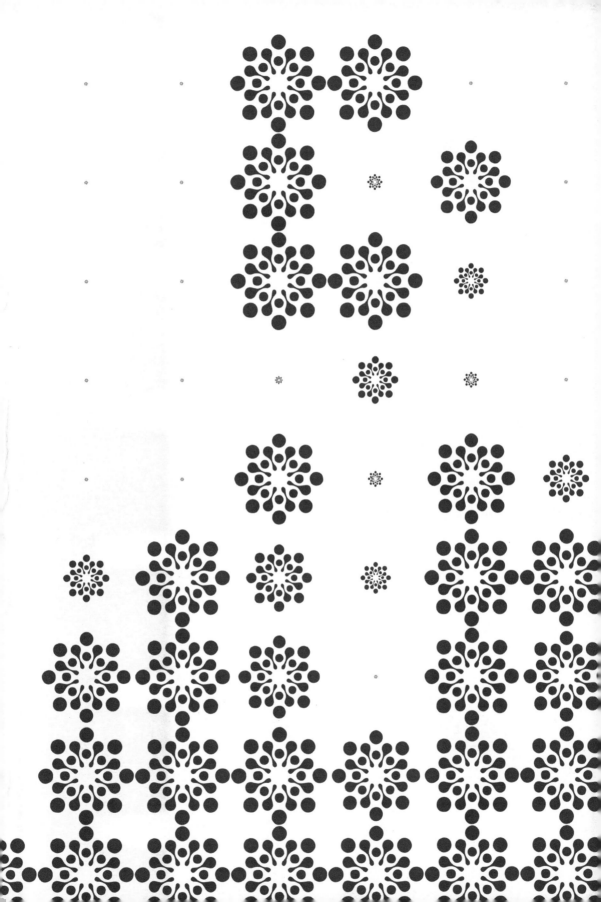

I discovered my head had changed over 19 years ago and always found it best to not talk about it.

About five years ago I had to medically retire from work, a difficult time. But I remembered from University I was a photojournalist and saw some amazing events taking some great pictures: Duke of Edinburgh to the Pope; two Presidents to a space shuttle. Now I am back to being a photographer, focusing on my friends, my family, my daughters and my great wife. It really helps me to forget my medical challenge and feel nearly normal.

The other day I took some commercial pictures for a care home and meet a lady who did not speak, but she gave me a card with a few words that help me forget my head:

Life is meant for joy and laughter
Life is like a day in Spring
With your hopes like white clouds racing
And your heart like birds that sing.

Added by my father on the 24th November 2019

Rebecca

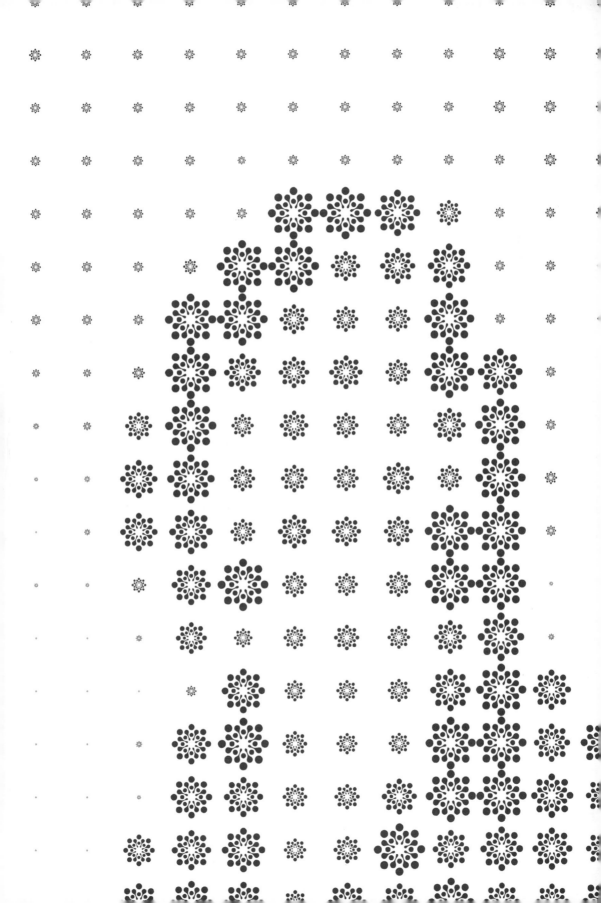

I was first diagnosed with cancer when I was just 38 years old, which was 30 weeks into my second pregnancy. I found the emotional impact of cancer extremely difficult to live with and it took many years to recover from this. This aspect of cancer needs to be talked about and supported, as soon as the diagnosis happens, so people can have a quality of life.

Jackie

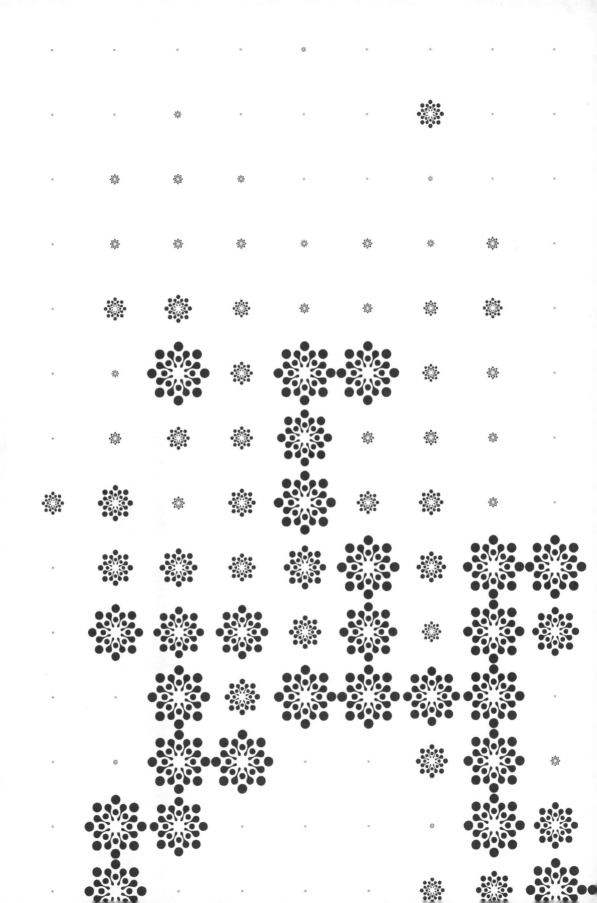

It is so important to talk openly. It not only helps you come to terms with the changes in your life, but helps the process of mentally adjusting to how you handle diagnosis, treatment and everyday life. I've stayed positive since my diagnosis in June 2018, but it's once chemotherapy finishes that you get days when the black cloud of recurrence hovers above you. It tries to break you mentally and physically.

Alison

My rare cancer (Adenoid Cystic Carcinoma) is always going to be with me, as it is incurable. I find that open conversation about any cancer is a good idea because it makes you feel like you are not alone. I belong to a few groups on social media and it is great to talk to people with the same cancer, especially if you have any worries or just want to chat.

Cindy

I was very unlucky to get breast cancer twice, first in 2016 then again in 2018. I have had both my breasts removed and feel fantastic. I carried on working all through my chemotherapy and radiotherapy. I had no side effects from any treatment, so I guess I was very lucky. I was very positive about it, talked about it and didn't want any sympathy. My husband, family and friends were always there for me.

Liz

I've been a cancer survivor for 30 years now – which is two thirds of my life – I was diagnosed at age 14. I now have nerve damage to my spinal nerve roots as a delayed radiation injury. The most important thing to me has been mental health support, opening up conversation and getting it out there, that cancer doesn't leave you once you're discharged from treatment. It never leaves you completely and for some, like me, the late effects of treatment can be worse than the original diagnosis.

Donna

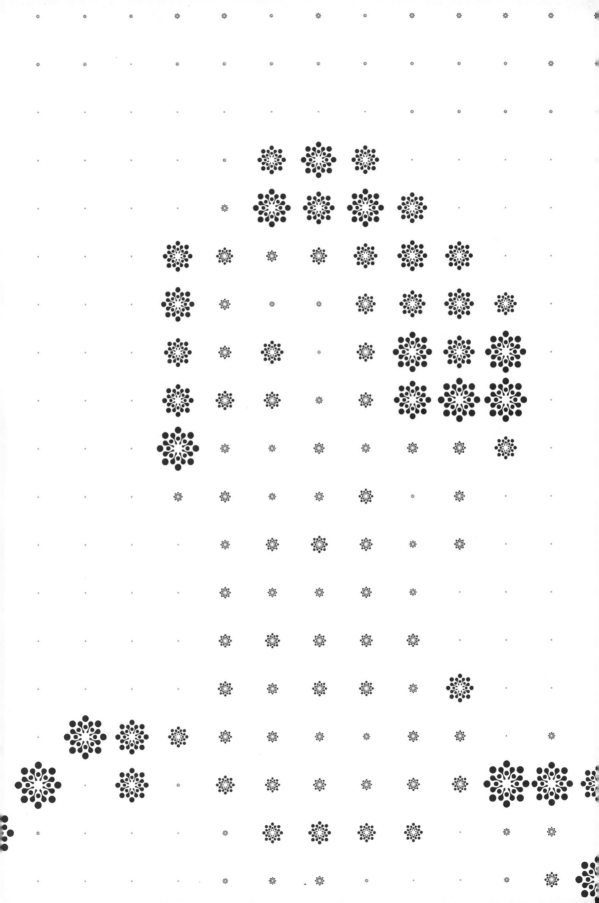

Cancer affected me by changing my family dynamics forever. It took away my eldest child aged just 18. She was meant to lead the way, be the trailblazer for the three younger ones. My perspective on life has changed. I don't tolerate people anymore. I want adventure. I crave achievements for others not myself. I want to improve cancer outcomes for others. So open conversation helps in an unimaginable way. The support network is incredible. The honesty and camaraderie is second to none. Understanding will save lives.

Georgie

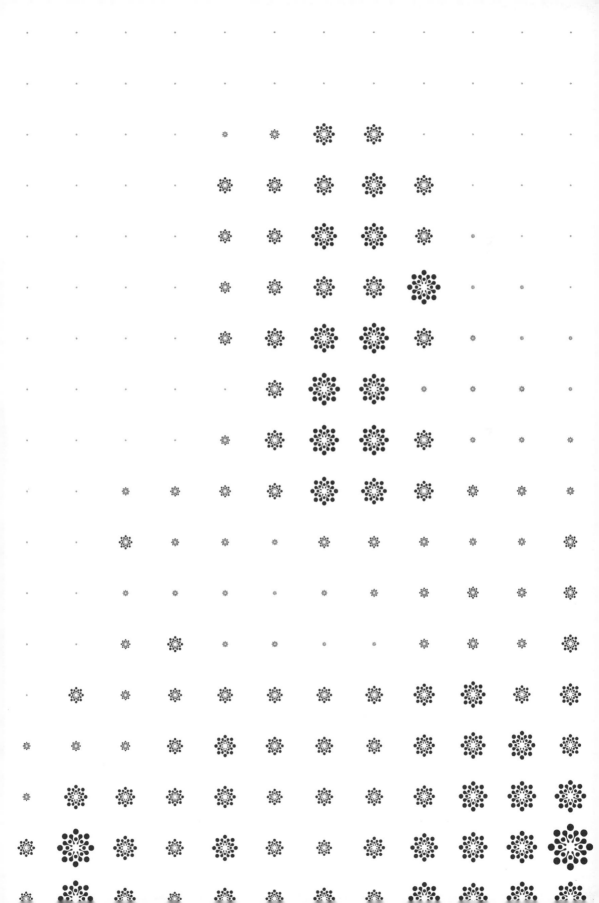

Cancer has made me more anxious but has also made me appreciate life. My grandmother used to mouth the word cancer as if it was a big and shameful secret. By talking about it and listening to podcasts it brings the whole conversation into the open.

Cancer is a very lonely journey and so to be able to share and read other people's stories, I personally found it incredibly helpful. I have found sharing my journey cathartic and have had really positive feedback from friends who wouldn't normally read a blog about cancer.

Alejandra

It's a complete game changer. It's made me stop worrying about the little things and enjoy every day. I hug my loved ones a bit tighter. People treat you like you are a wounded puppy and the reality is that you want to be normal, you are still you, just with cancer. I started a blog, as a way to vent and it has helped people around me to understand how I am feeling. There is a huge online cancer community, where I have found comfort and heaps of information, from people going through the same.

Barbara

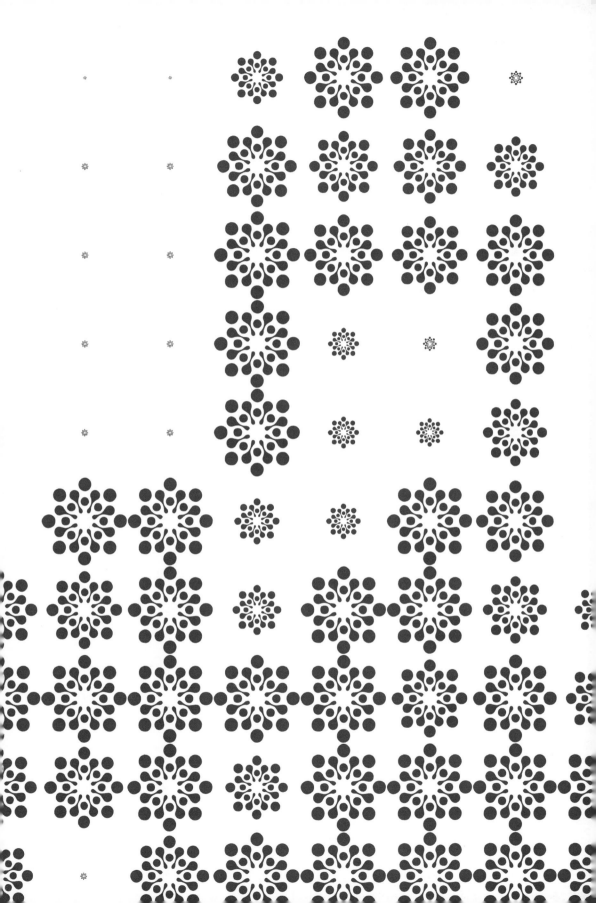

Cancer has affected my life in every single aspect. Some good, some bad. But I tell you what, it's made me stronger and absolutely cherish every single minute of every single day. Just talk about it. Nothing anyone can say or do can make you feel any better or worse. So just speak. Don't do the head tilts with the 'Aaawww are you okay?'. 'No I'm not'. But that's just going to make you feel worse! Social media has I think normalized it. It's not so much of a taboo subject, it's part of everyday life, as is Facebook, Twitter, Instagram etc.

Tasha

Natasha was a true inspiration to all who met her. At 16 years old, in 2007, she was diagnosed with an inoperable brain tumour and told she had nine to twelve months to live. She lived for eight years. Due to raised intracranial pressure her optic nerves were damaged, which left her blind. She embraced her disability, learning to cope with all the daily challenges life threw at her. Not only did she cope with the harsh treatment needed, she never stopped smiling and making those around her smile. As her Uncle, Will, said in the tribute he wrote about his niece: 'actually, Tasha didn't just touch hearts, she stole them.'

Written by Shona, Tasha's mother

Becca

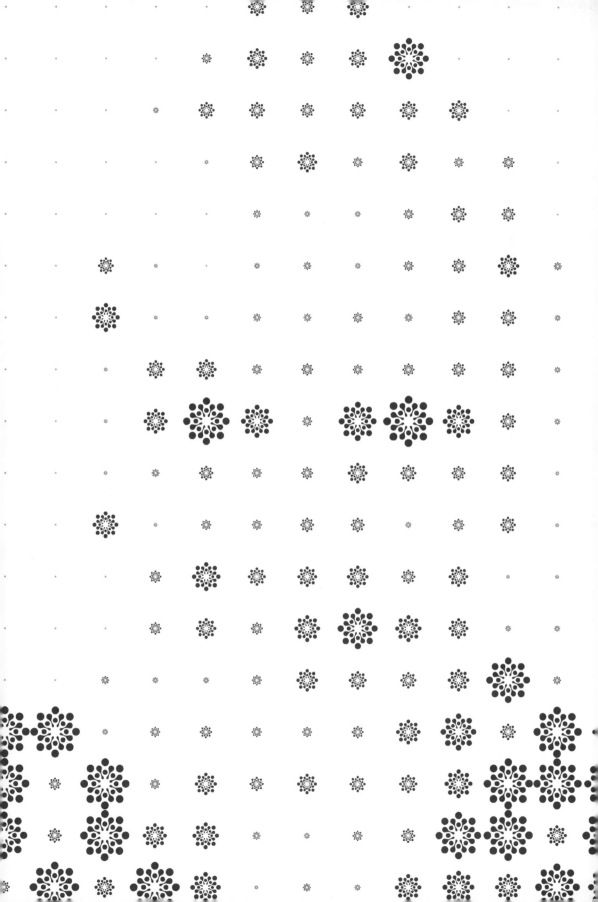

I was diagnosed with inflammatory triple negative breast cancer in May 2017 at the age of 38 and it's completely changed my life in every way. I have had a double mastectomy, which coupled with losing my hair due to chemotherapy made me feel unfeminine. I am stronger than I ever knew I was capable of.

I think it's so important to be open and honest about how rubbish having cancer is but you can get through it. I am completely open about every part of my treatment to remove any stigmas. I have a blog and have found that it's been invaluable to me in letting my family and friends know what's going on.

Sarah

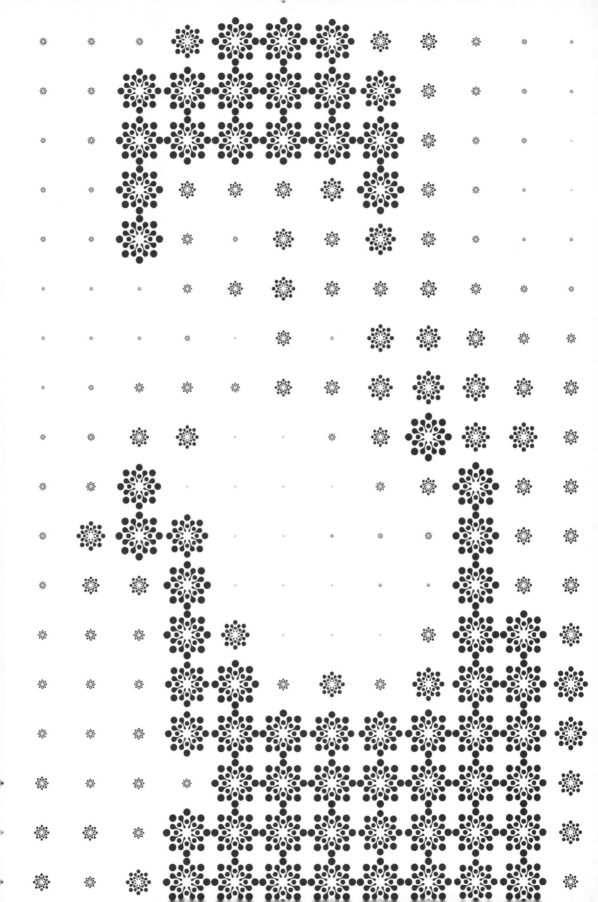

I was treated for cervical cancer five years ago. Radiotherapy treatment left me with Pelvic Radiation Disease which has been life changing. I now have a permanent colostomy and urostomy, which you would never know just by looking at me. Looks can be deceiving, we have no idea what other people are going through. Not all disabilities and illnesses are visible.

The effects of cancer and cancer treatment can continue for the rest of your life which is why it's important to be open about cancer and continue to talk, long after treatment has ended. I feel very privileged to be able to speak out as a patient advocate as I understand how important it is to raise awareness and start a conversation about what it's like to live with and beyond cancer.

Lucy

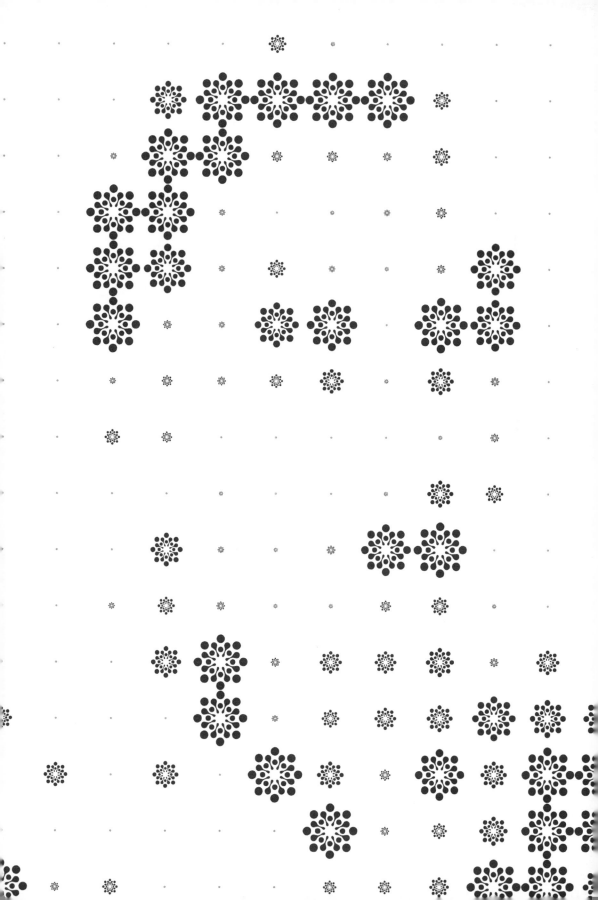

I was diagnosed with Non-Hodgkin's Lymphoma 23rd March 2018. It is the most common cancer for under 30s and yet I knew nothing about it. This is exactly why more awareness and open discussions are needed around cancer. One in two of us will be diagnosed with cancer in our lifetime; that is the scary but true statistic. This disease doesn't discriminate, it doesn't care if you are rich or poor, if you own a dog, if you hate the colour yellow, if you have kids, if you want to travel the world. We need to break down the barriers and end the stigma so that people don't feel quite so alone. Yes cancer is scary, but for 50% of the population, including me currently, it is their version of normal.

Nicola

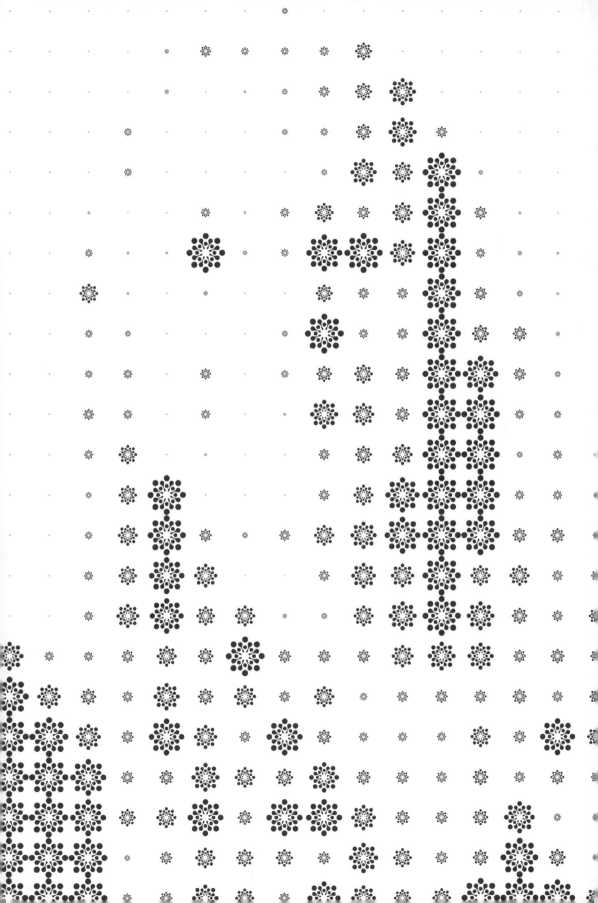

Cancer has taught me many lessons, including patience, kindness and taking time to just think and look around at all that you have been missing while rushing around. This is huge and yes could last for hours. For me I say it's happening to so many people so let's just be open about it and share the good and the bad. Give others support, including family members who are dealing with the caring and picking up all the slack now. Social media, when used for good, is such an amazing tool. I have connected with hundreds of people in the same situation as me. This gives huge support when you need it and for those who can't get out or are living alone – it can also be a lifesaver. Cancer is a lonely road at times even when you are surrounded by people. Get up, show up and never give up.

Andrew

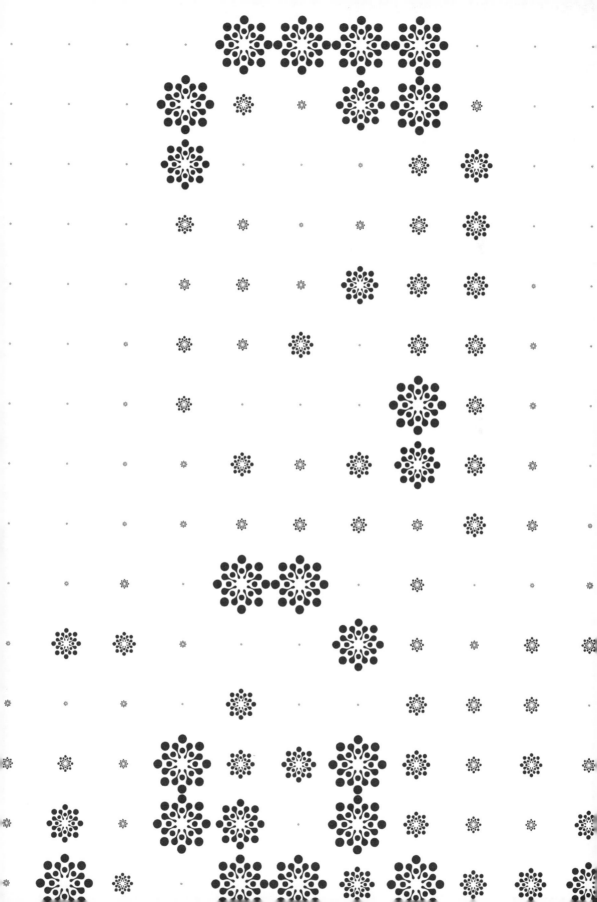

Andrew was diagnosed with Acute Lymphoblastic Leukaemia aged three and five months. His treatment lasted for 1235 days. I kept a diary throughout his treatment. I logged this on Facebook, for all to see and share. I was determined, and still am, to be open and honest about cancer, but also to show that children survive cancer. Leukaemia is no longer a death sentence because awareness = money = research = cure.

I have made many firm friends through Twitter and Facebook groups. We speak virtually and occasionally meet up. The Bloodwise #feelalivefriday tweets kept me focused on the positive and built my following. I then created a crowdfunding campaign to raise money to self-publish my story. I raised £1200 in 24 hours, as so many people believed in the power of the message. I continue to 'tell the story', even though we are three years since the end of Andrew's treatment.

Written by Melody, Andrew's mother

Joanna

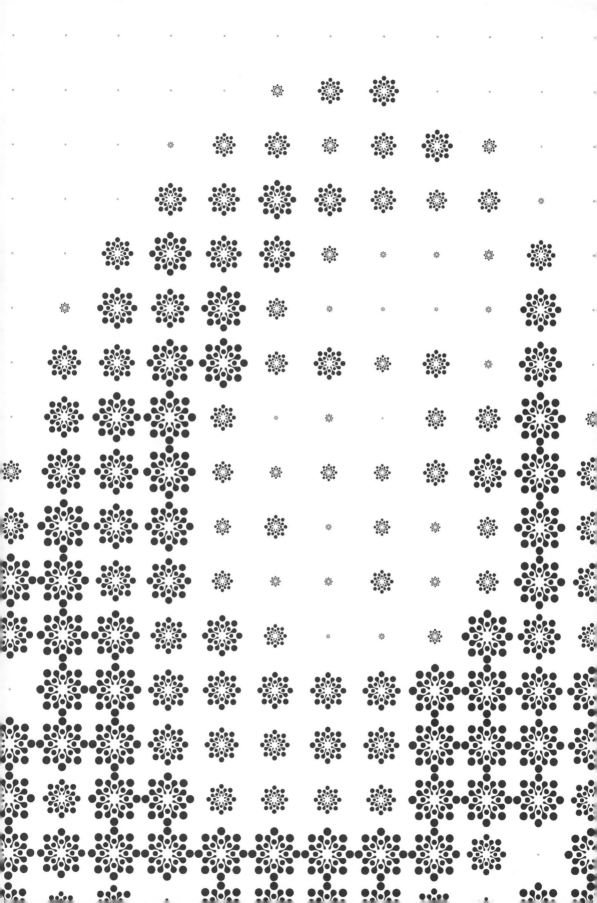

I have Chronic Myeloid Leukaemia (CML), with the T315i mutation. I think it's really important to have more conversations about cancer because sadly it affects so many of us. CML is a rare blood cancer, and the mutation I have is even rarer. So that's why I have found online groups really valuable because otherwise I would feel more isolated and be less likely to meet someone face-to-face with the same disease. By having conversations about cancer, some of the fear and isolation can be reduced.

I had to have a bone marrow transplant because of the CML, which was a huge thing for me and my family. Unfortunately the transplant didn't work properly so I had to go back on the oral chemotherapy drugs which control the CML. Plus the drugs, as well as the transplant, have led to various side effects. But I'm so very thankful to be here and have a second chance of life.

Nikki

I was first diagnosed with cancer in 1991 (19 years old) and later in 2016. So I've actually been alive longer with cancer in my life than being cancer free! Cancer I believe has had a huge impact on me, I'm quite an anxious person and quite fearful. But cancer has given me tremendous strength and has made me passionate about life.

I believe we should talk more about cancer, it sadly is a part of life, but that's just it. It's part of life, not the end of life (even those who have a terminal diagnosis are living well with their diagnosis until the very end). The more we talk, share and learn, the more we empower people to not see it as a death sentence – it's liberating. I believe we need to remove the energy from the word cancer.

For me social media connects me to others. It makes me feel normal whatever I'm feeling that day as I know someone somewhere is experiencing something similar. It gives me courage to be me.

Bridget

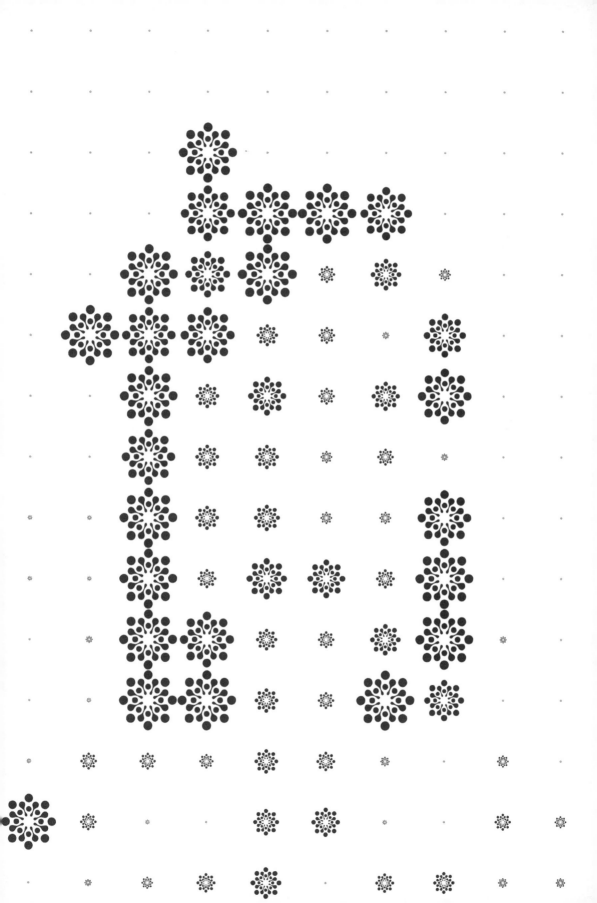

Cancer has put my life on hold. I've been affected twice in the last year and a half, with two major operations and currently undergoing chemotherapy. It's stolen precious time with my two young children, strained my relationship with my husband, affected my mental health and delayed my return to work. I hate not feeling like me. Until I was diagnosed, cancer wasn't something we ever talked about as a family or with friends. Why is this? Since being diagnosed I realise how many people's lives have been affected. How many people have lost loved ones and how brutal the treatment is. The more we can learn and talk about cancer, the better. I want my children to grow up not being scared of cancer but being aware of it.

For me the internet and social media has been a huge platform for support, advice and information. I have heard people's stories that I would never have had access to without the internet. While the NHS has been great, it's so overstretched it is unable to provide all the necessary support to a cancer patient.

Christine

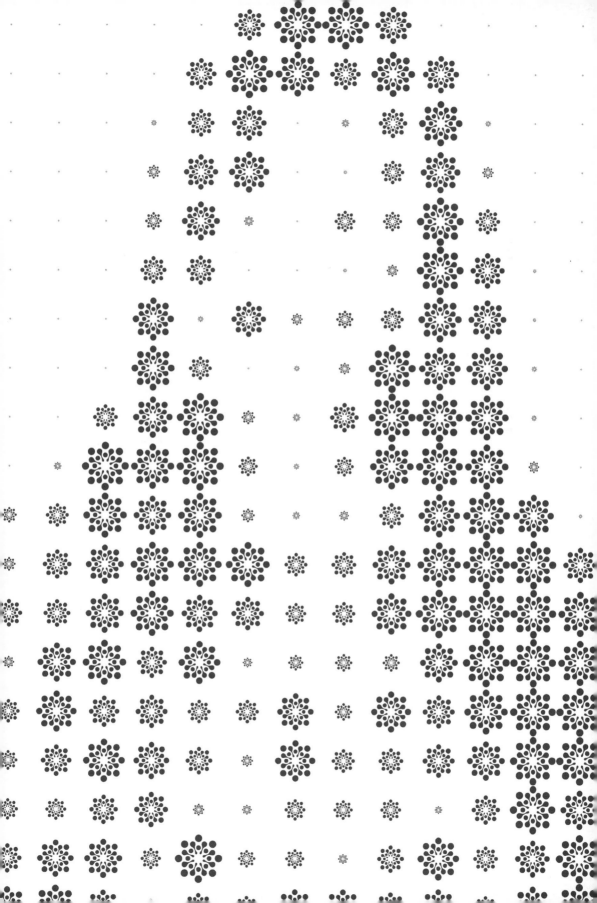

Cancer has affected me massively. My old life feels like it was a different lifetime. I've now been left with so many ailments. Right-sided weakness, balance problems (I have to walk with a stick), permanent double vision, short term memory problems, difficulties with processing information. Because of all these problems I've become so reclusive and my circle of friends is very small now. I now suffer from anxiety and hate group situations. And to make it worse I have no emotional support because of my Asian culture and English is not my parent's first language. I feel so alone.

It is so important for open conversation to normalise the cancer discussion. I've found a lot of people don't know how to react when you bring up the topic or when they hear the word cancer, they think you have a death sentence and get quite scared.

I think social media has been good for normalising cancer, you see all these young adults out doing what young adults do, but they also live with cancer at the same time.

Jane

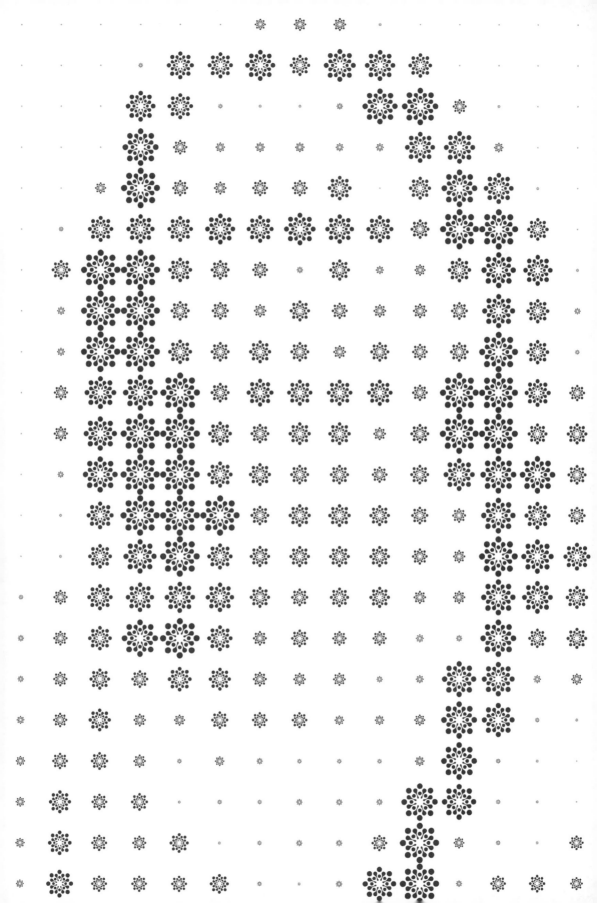

I am 45 years old. I am married and I have two young children. I was diagnosed with Acute Myeloid Leukaemia (AML) in December 2014. I achieved remission but then relapsed very quickly. I then had further chemotherapy and a stem cell transplant in February 2016. I remain in remission but I live with life changing side effects from my treatment. I also lost my mother to a brain tumour in 1997. I'm now an Ambassador for the charity Bloodwise.

My cancer diagnosis came like a smack in the face. In an instant my life was turned upside down and my strong, fearless body became fragile and vulnerable. I was no longer able to be the wife and mother I wanted to be.

Talking to my children openly about my diagnosis, and how it has changed me, has been a vital part of coping. By being honest and open with them it has given them the confidence to speak up about their fears and how they have been affected. It has helped them to not be afraid. We have been able to accept our new normal and move on.

Laura

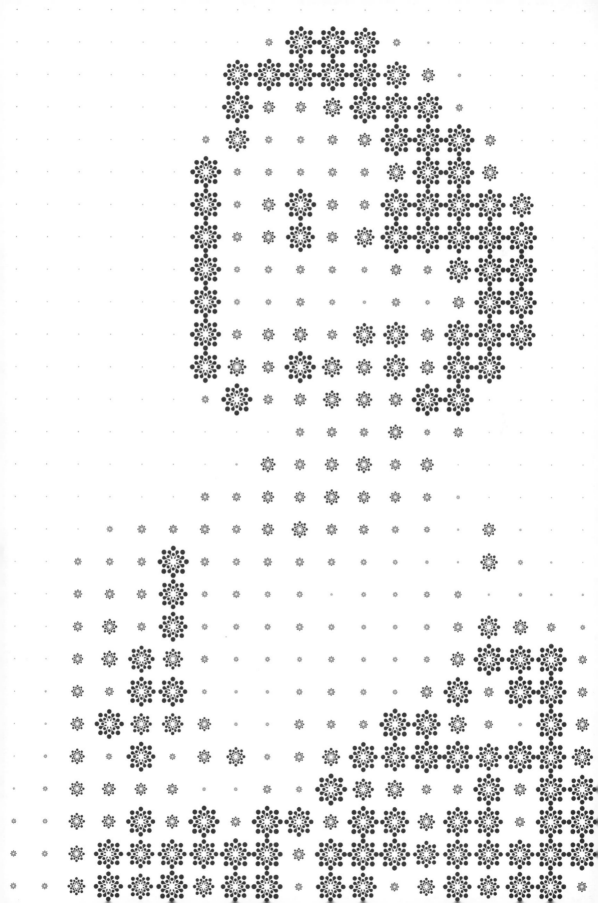

022

In 2014, when I was 25 years old, I discovered I had primary breast cancer after finding a lump in my left breast. I endured chemotherapy, a mastectomy, radiotherapy and hormonal treatments which put me into remission. But only a short time later my cancer returned to my bones meaning I was now incurable. I went through further treatment and operations to try and stop further spread of the disease and I am currently on regular treatment, both in the hospital and at home, which are keeping me stable.

It is so important to open up conversation about cancer because knowing what signs and symptoms are for each type could save lives. Cancer is a hugely complex disease which needs discussing so people understand it more.

In today's world, social media is amazing in many ways. It helps to open up these conversations which people never use to have, it helps connect you to others going through similar things and it makes you feel less alone. People these days share their stories and their experiences, which in turn, helps others cope with their diagnosis. It is a hugely valuable tool, if used correctly.

Nikki

023

I was diagnosed with stage 3 hormone positive breast cancer in March 2017, which was very scary at the time. How do you tell your loved ones you have cancer? No one wants to deliver a sentence with the word cancer in it – it's the equivalent of telling kids there's no Santa. I had the full regime for primary breast cancer; chemotherapy, surgery and radiotherapy, which took almost a year to complete. After finishing treatment I came out feeling quite lost with feelings that I had to try and carry on as 'normal'. In reality some of your old self remains lost; the carefree part of you. Cancer gave me a harsh reality card that I am a mortal being. It was like plunging my head into the murky depths of a dark underwater world which I cannot unsee.

It's not all bad though, as I gained a perspective on life which enabled me to focus on what's important. I became very anxious about planning ahead as I feared my cancer may return and I'd need to be available for treatment. I'm learning to optimistically put events on my calendar and by doing so it frees the mind and opens a world of opportunity.

Cristina

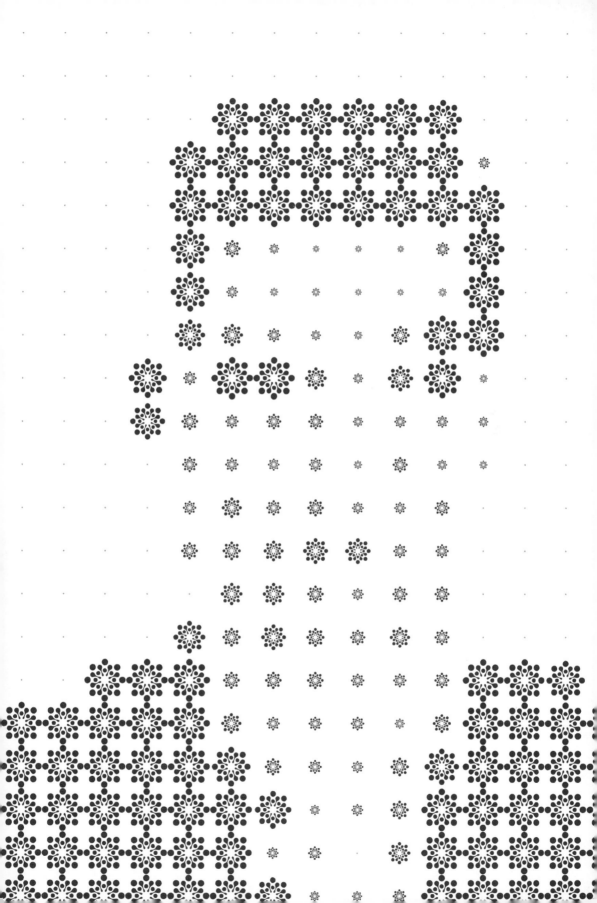

024

I was treated for breast cancer. This journey changed me, as I dared to be me. I don't mind what people think or say. I don't care anymore about 'should be'. I dare to choose what I like, what makes me happy. I dare to try new things. In a way, I blossomed. Cheesy but that's how I feel it. The future is wide open. I resumed my hobbies and wish to give back to the community. I work on my bucket list, because I'm alive.

That's urgent and that's what I try to do with The Cancer Majlis. Cancer shouldn't be a taboo. The more we talk about it, less taboo. Less taboo, less fear to talk about it and more people go to their screenings. Less people die from cancer today thanks to screening, so let's share the good news. We also need to tackle the topics of cancer at work, post cancer life, including family planning post cancer, sexuality post cancer, applying for mortgage post cancer, medical insurance and pre-existing conditions coverage. If we are getting cancer at a younger age, we need help to resume and keep on living our lives normally.

The Cancer Majlis includes inspirational, fun and informative posts about cancer life. For all lives touched by cancer: patients, family and friends, colleagues. Basically everyone.

Charlene

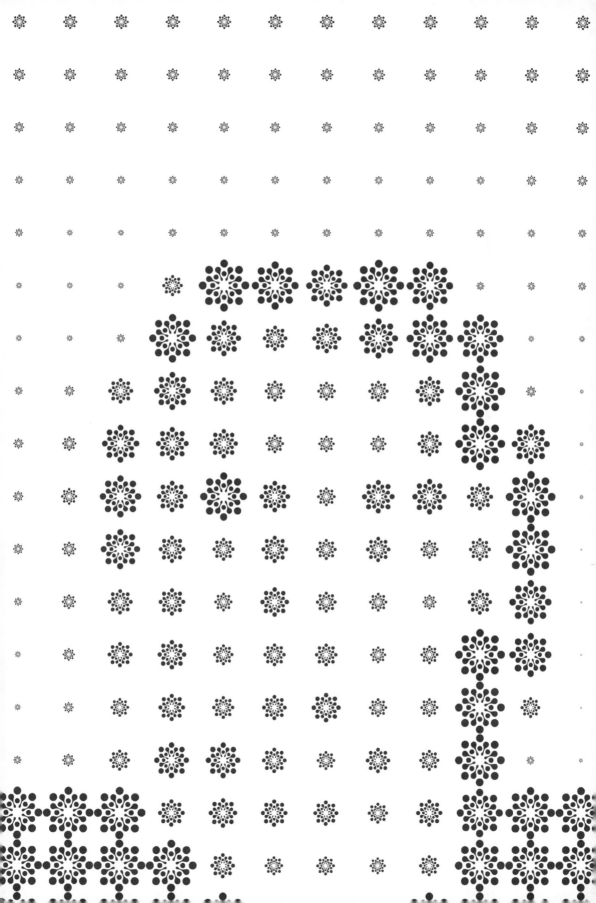

025

My name is Charlene and I have stage 4 bowel cancer that has spread to my liver. I was diagnosed in April 2017 when my youngest daughter was eight months old. I naively thought that cancer was something other people got, I never imagined it would happen to me. When I was diagnosed my whole life flipped upside down. I am married with four children and life as we knew it was over. Life now revolves around hospital appointments, surgeries and treatments. Although cancer has been the hardest thing I have ever had to face, it has also made me open my eyes to the wonderful things my life already had. It has made me a hundred times more grateful for them.

It's so important we have open conversations about cancer. I thought I knew what cancer was and I thought I knew the symptoms but cancer is not always a lump (as my mind had previously let me believe). When cancer isn't openly spoken about, nor are the symptoms. It also makes it difficult to have conversations with family and friends once you're diagnosed because it's such a taboo subject. Nobody knows how to communicate on the subject and are often left saying nothing because they fear what they do say could be wrong.

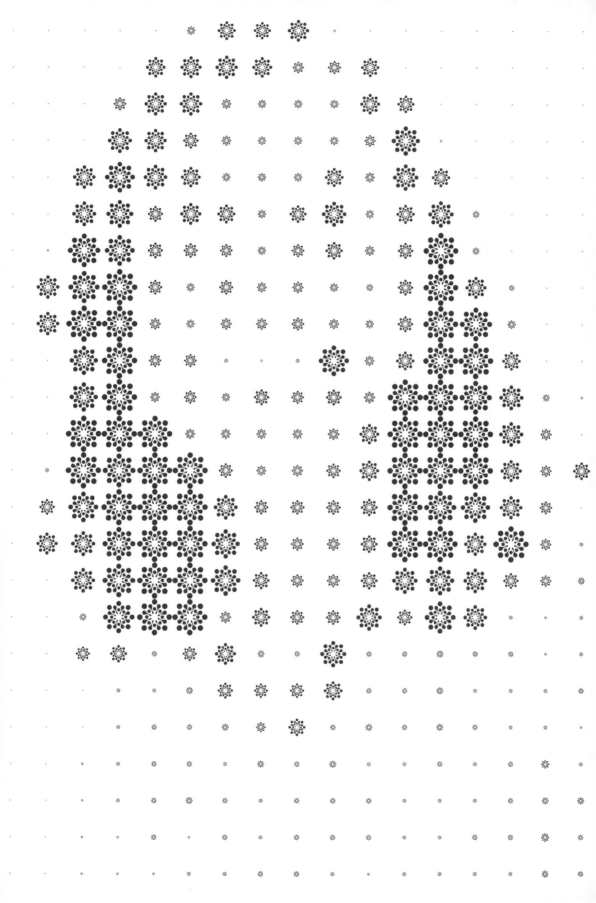

026

Cancer has impacted me and my family in a monumental way. Firstly, my husband was diagnosed with lymphoma and then on holiday, as we were celebrating the end of his cancer journey, I discovered a lump in my breast. So I went on to be treated for breast cancer. We had only been married for 18 months when he was diagnosed. To say this turned our world upside down would be an understatement. We both had to face our mortality, we had to endure horrendous treatment regimes and we had to find a way to navigate the pain. The pain that we were facing individually, as a couple, as a carer for the other, and the pain of some of our dreams never being realised.

Whilst cancer has been the unwelcome visitor in our lives, it's also been the gift that made us wake up and embrace a new way of living, a new way of thriving. It has bought us gratitude, faith, hope and a richness that we hadn't felt before. Cancer will sadly affect all of us in some way in our lifetime. We need to know that we are seen and heard and that we matter, and we need to know how we can still maintain some level of control in whatever life throws at us.

Jolene

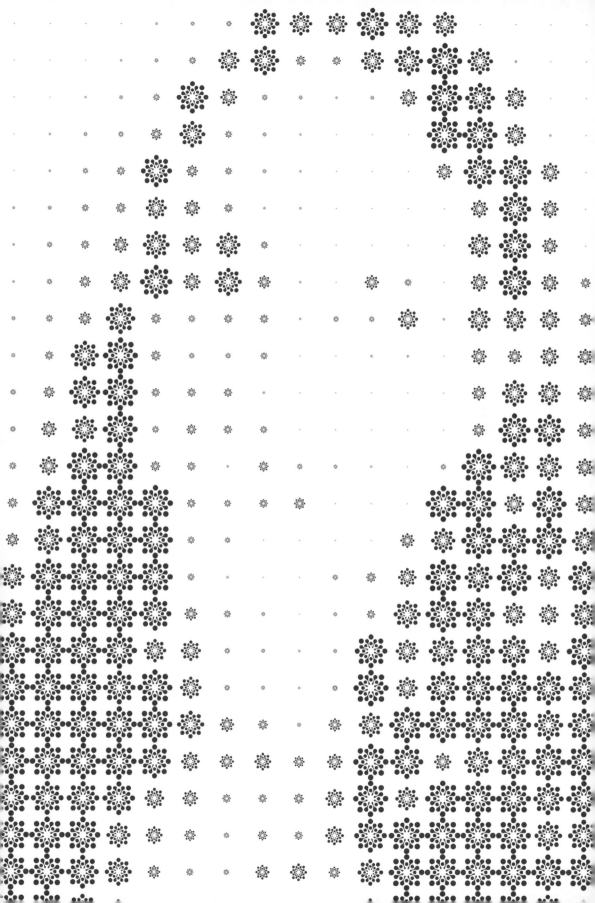

027

I've been living with stage 4 melanoma since 2010. I was told my life expectancy would be 18 months when it was discovered – I had a brain tumour and a lung tumour not long after finishing university. Advances in treatment for melanoma have meant I am still alive today. I just finished four and a half years of systemic treatment and two and a half of that was on the immunotherapy drug Pembrolizumab. When I was initially diagnosed with stage 4 cancer, there were no other treatments I could have except surgery. So I count myself very lucky! I am now on 'watch and wait' since January this year which seemed completely unrealistic even a few months ago.

So cancer has had an effect on my life since the day I was initially diagnosed at the age of 18. It's a huge part of life and it will never cease to exist. It's taken a lot from me, not just in the physical sense but also affected my confidence in so many ways.

It is important to continue the conversation because statistics indicated: One in two people will experience cancer in their lifetime. It's a scary statistic but so much is being done to develop more effective treatments. We need to talk about it in the same way as a cold, rather than it being seen as a taboo subject. I think this would help with earlier diagnosis.

Sylvia

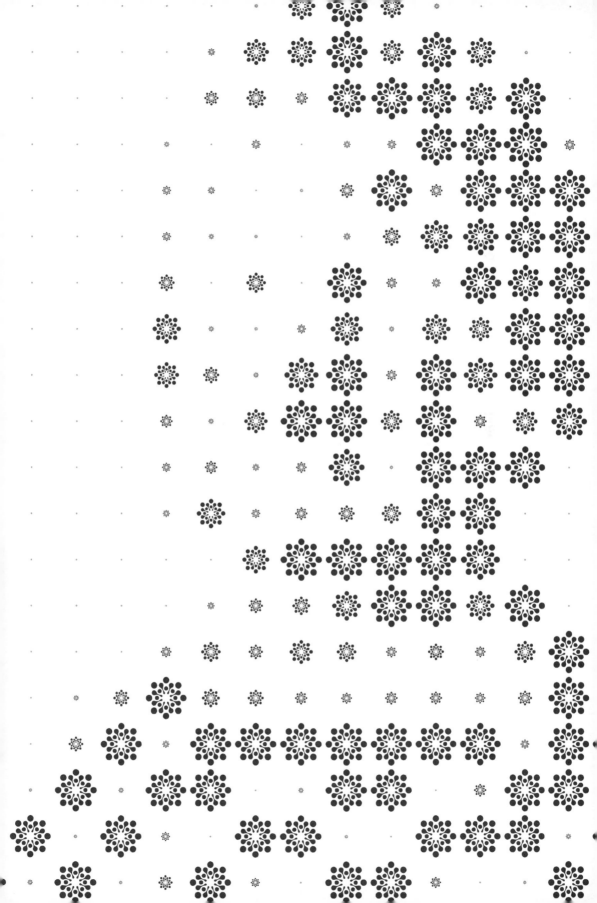

028

When you hear the words being said, that your husband has cancer – Acute Lymphoblastic Leukaemia, which is blood cancer – the world folds up around you. You go numb. Then it all rushes back like a river in a flood and the questions start. It's easier to talk it over with those close to you, but much harder to discuss things with people outside that circle. People always say how sorry they are – sorry for what? And then it's often followed by 'how is he doing?' How do you explain to people that cancer lives alongside you forever? So the usual response is 'he is fine'. It's just easier. But talking starts to put cancer into perspective, it helps you to cope and in doing so helps others understand. But they shy away in case you tell them something awful, even though they do care.

I joined an online group for my husband's specific blood cancer. Sharing the fears, talking about concerns, and reading other open and frank responses really helped me come to terms with what's happening in our life. It is hard to see the sadness in people's eyes when you realise what you are telling them – your husband has cancer. So the anonymity of social media shields that reaction. People should talk more, so cancer patients and their carers are not going to break down all the time. I'm a Bloodwise Ambassador too, which helps.

Robert

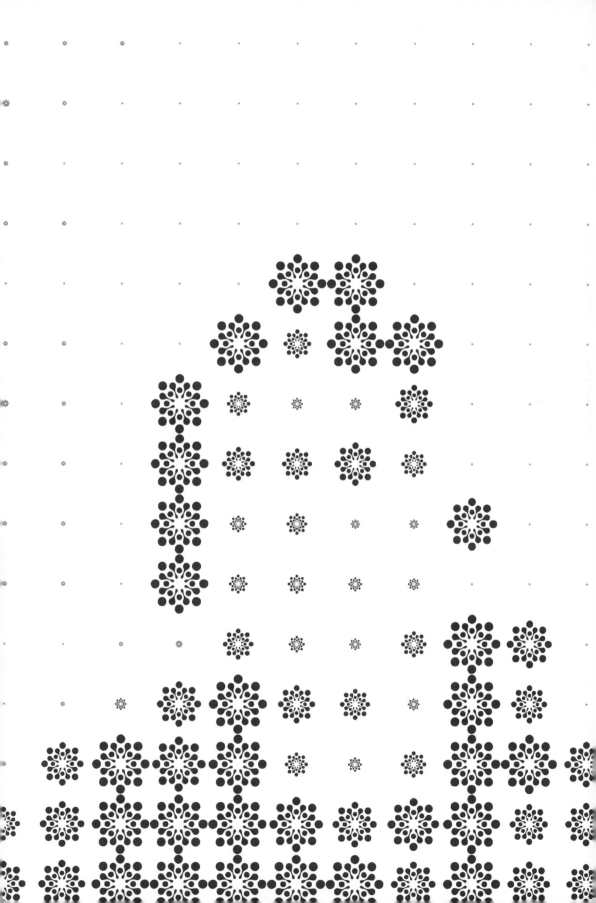

029

Having cancer has really affected my mental health, it has brought anger and anxiety to the forefront of my emotions. I have been using techniques to work on these issues and thankfully they are working. Also it has had a big impact on my perspective of life, of what's important and what's not.

As someone who has been very open about my cancer and how it has affected me, it has helped me deal with my diagnosis and made it a very normal thing to talk about. If I, or the people around me didn't discuss it, there would be a lot of awkwardness involved with the conversation. Being able to talk about it freely is definitely beneficial as a cancer patient.

Social media has been the best part for me, being able to voice how I'm feeling and raising awareness at the same time. If I need to off-load I can use my social media to vent and at the same time it lets people know what it's actually like to live with cancer. People respond differently to each post, everyone is supportive but in different ways. You have the people who religiously tell you to be strong and then the people who may be in a similar situation who tell their story, which in turn is helping talk about the cancer journey. I always like to know how others dealt with the situation.

Charlotte

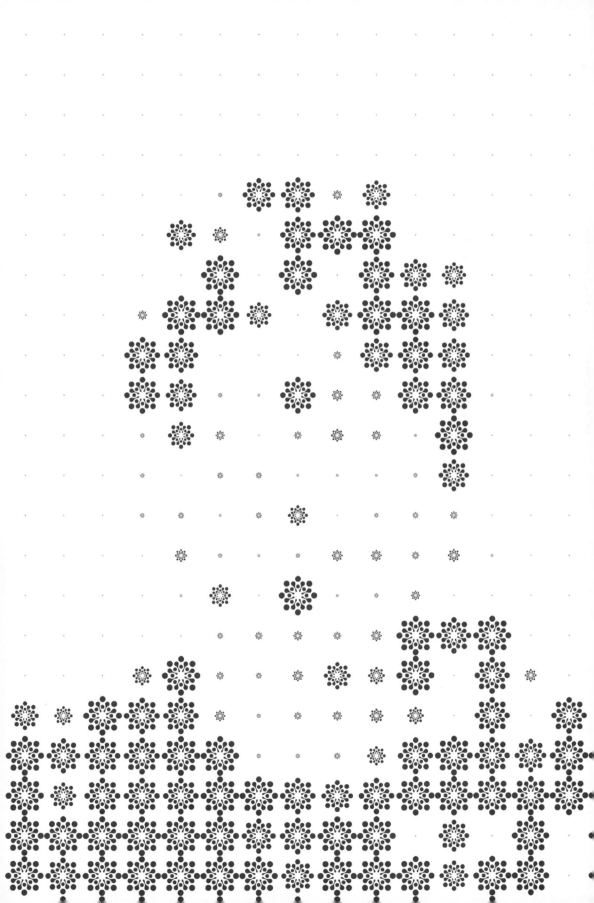

030

Cancer has made me realise how little control we have over many aspects of our lives and how precious it is to have a resemblance of normality when you can. So often, we strive for everything to be perfect, but actually, if everything is under vague control, that's more than enough to be happy about! It's also made me very thankful for the people I have around me. Going through this on my own would have been so much harder.

Cancer is common and its effects (both from the disease and its treatment) are brutal, both physically and psychologically. There is probably no one who can say that they have never met someone affected by cancer. As a person with cancer, your day can be made easier by someone saying the right thing. On the other hand your day can be made harder by a comment that might be well meaning, but misses the mark. I found people saying 'it'll grow back', with respect to my hair, very frustrating and at times upsetting. Normalising these issues might make people more aware of how to phrase things, or topics best left alone.

I've really loved how social media connects people in the cancer community. I've met some fantastic people who understand what I'm going through. Plus, having other people to celebrate milestones with, is encouraging. I think this is particularly relevant as a younger person with cancer, as often the people you meet at the chemotherapy unit are much older.

Natalia

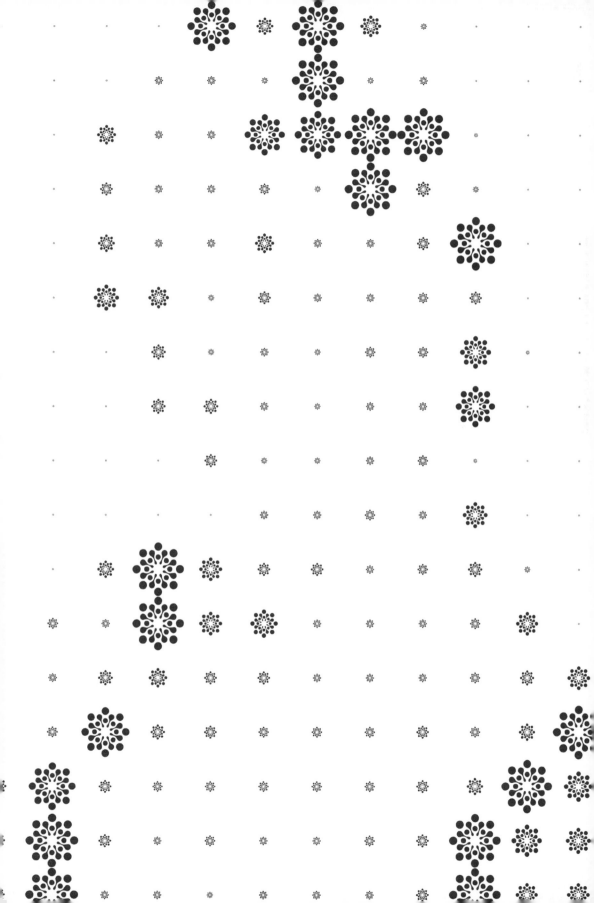

031

I have stage 2 Hodgkin's Lymphoma, unfavourable with a bulky mass (17cm) in my chest. It was definitely a shock to hear this news at the start of the New Year, after the rough year I had already, this was icing on the cake. At first I was more worried about the stress I was going to cause for other people, I didn't really think about how this would change my life and my outlook. Once it all hit me I was terrified, but more numb than anything. As I started treatment and allowed myself to start transforming into a better version of me, my whole outlook changed and the fighter in me came out. I am still struggling with some hard days, but trying to find the positives in each moment. We are only given what we can handle, this will only make me stronger and I can't wait to see who I've become once I beat this!

Open conversation is so important. It allows people to connect and not have to feel scared or judged for what they're thinking and feeling. Once you see that you're not alone, you start to feel better and less trapped. It lets you get out everything that's weighing you down and get different perspectives on certain topics. My blog has allowed me to connect with so many people going through a similar situation. Social media has become such a great community and outlet whilst going through this.

Catherine

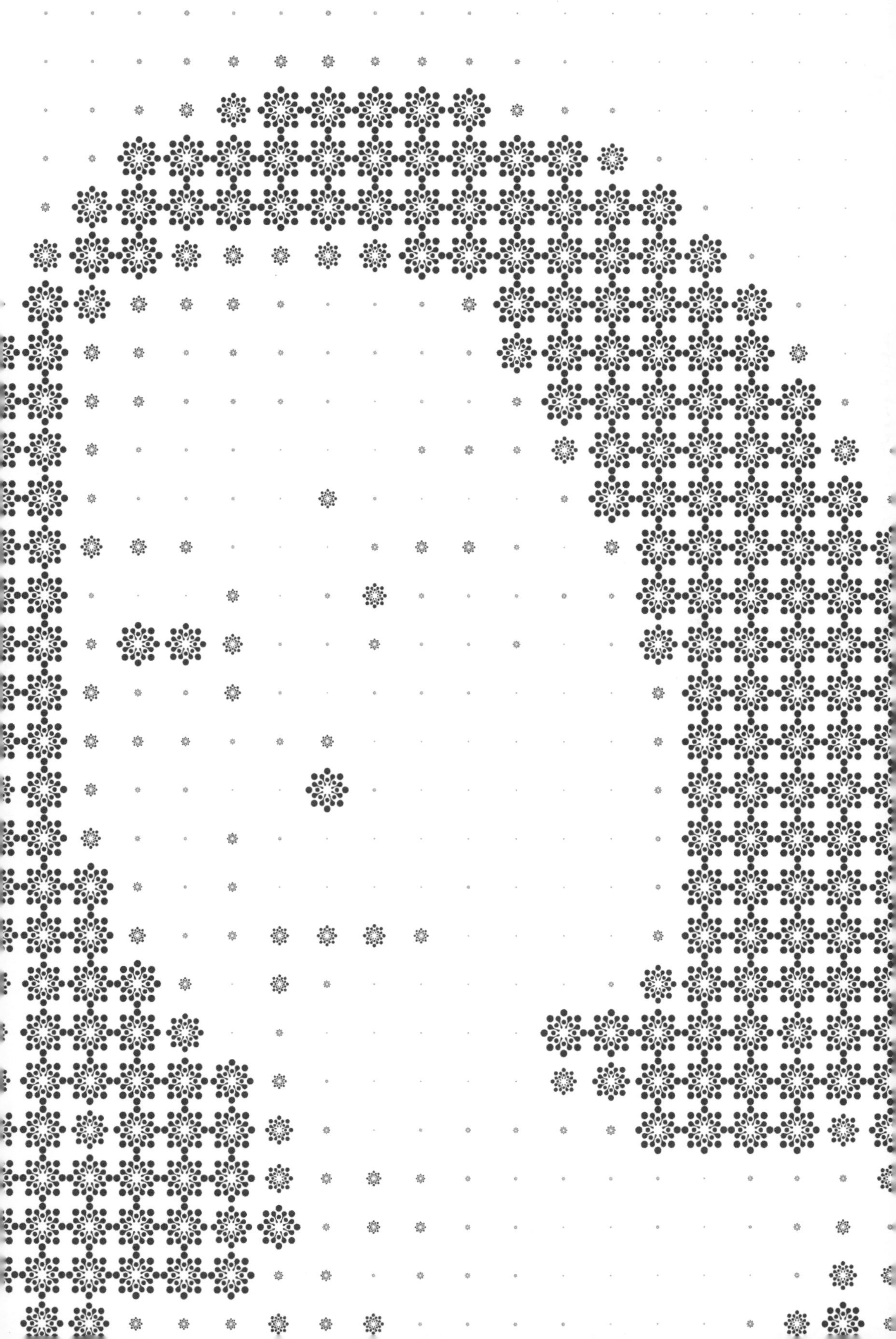

032

Cancer shattered me and my life wide open. I cracked into a million bits during treatment. My kids were two and four years old. Would I see their next birthdays? This thought haunted me every day throughout treatment. I was strong and independent one week, then suddenly I was weak, totally reliant on others and facing my own mortality. That changes you. It changes your relationships. It changes everything forever more. People get funny around cancer. Some don't know how to talk to a loved one with cancer and so avoid the subject, or worse, they avoid the person altogether!

Open conversation takes the mystery out of it. It makes everyone involved feel more comfortable talking about the illness and how it makes you feel, whether you are the person with cancer or are on the side of wanting to support and talk to a loved one with cancer. This can only be a good thing.

I found my cancer tribe on Twitter. I gave an honest account of what was happening to me and was heartened to hear from those in the same position as I was. I posted about the good and the bad, which I think assisted those close to me to hear about what was happening without having to ask. During treatment this was good as I was too sick to repeat these things. Post treatment my openness on Twitter meant people felt comfortable talking to me about cancer as it was all out in public anyway.

Gillian

033

In 2017 just before Christmas I had a biopsy, to see if I had breast cancer. Then just before the New Year I was told I did! I then had surgery in February, chemotherapy in April and Herceptin (targeted therapy) up until now. Things have been a bit complicated during my treatment. I am allergic to one of my chemotherapy drugs – I had some heart issues and hypersensitivity to targeted therapy, so the side effects have been quite intrusive.

I have just finished treatment, it hasn't really sunk in yet and the side effects are still with me. I am hoping they will pass or diminish as time passes. I am very grateful to the NHS for their excellent care and expertise. A lot needs to happen to help people overcome their fears about cancer – some people I considered to be my friends have disappeared from my life when they heard the word cancer. Work and my colleagues have been really supportive and I'm lucky to have a wonderful family too. New Twitter and Facebook friends have helped so much as a support network. It's a way to stay connected, to stay in touch with the world when I felt isolated, and also to keep involved and to have other interests even when I lacked energy to get out and about.

When I spoke to Helena we talked about processes, and I have found the treatment process fascinating. It has been a learning curve too: discovering about cancer and how individual treatment is for each person. Twitter and Facebook have proved invaluable information for that too. Please note: no battles or wars have been fought during my treatment.

Ginny

034

I was diagnosed with breast cancer in early January 2019. Cancer has affected other, more distant members of my family in the last 30 years, but my diagnosis at the young age of 25 was quite unexpected. Open conversation about cancer is so important for awareness, early detection and understanding (as both a patient and as a friend/ally). Normalising discussion about cancer is so important so that nobody has to go through cancer alone. A couple of friends have had trouble even saying the word 'cancer' confidently. Almost like it's a swear word or Voldemort, which makes talking about it a bit tricky. Cancer is obviously personal to each person who is diagnosed and also to their families, and how open or chatty they wish to be about it. Everyone experiences and deals with cancer in varied ways so having more discussion can help not only those affected, but also those who can give support – even if it's just sending a good phrase in a greeting card.

I think that social media and the internet has been a great help for open discussion about cancer. Not only has it helped me to connect with other people's experiences, it has shown me what to expect, as well as top tips for coping with a diagnosis or side effects. It has helped my friends, because they can look up/ Google my experience and learn everything they need to know. Then I don't have to repeat draining and emotional conversations or medical information, which can be so difficult.

Lizzie

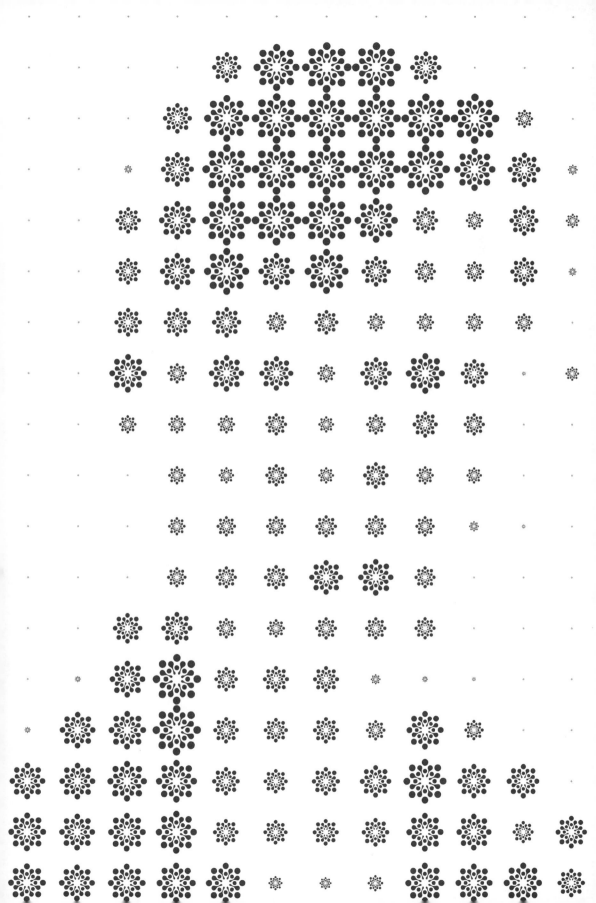

035

Cancer has affected every aspect of my life. There will now always be a 'before cancer' and an 'after cancer'. At times over the last five years since my original diagnosis, I have had to change what I eat and where I go due to my compromised immune system. I lost all independence due to weakness and fatigue. I had to rely on other people and because of this, I lost confidence in myself.

Open conversation about cancer is the only way to normalise the subject – it is normal for the people going through it. They will have to adapt to their 'new normal' throughout their cancer journey, and it doesn't just stop when the treatment is over – there are long-lasting medical and emotional effects. I know most people just don't want to offend or upset and everyone is different, so I think it often falls to the cancer patient themselves to set the tone with those around them on what they are comfortable talking about.

Social media and the internet can be a really positive place. It might be the only way to connect with people who are in the same situation as you and therefore know exactly what you are going through; whereas maybe your friends and family don't. Cancer is as normal to them as it is for you and talking to other patients helped me accept the changes that come with it. Also, seeing the bravery and hope of others can inspire you to keep going.

Angela

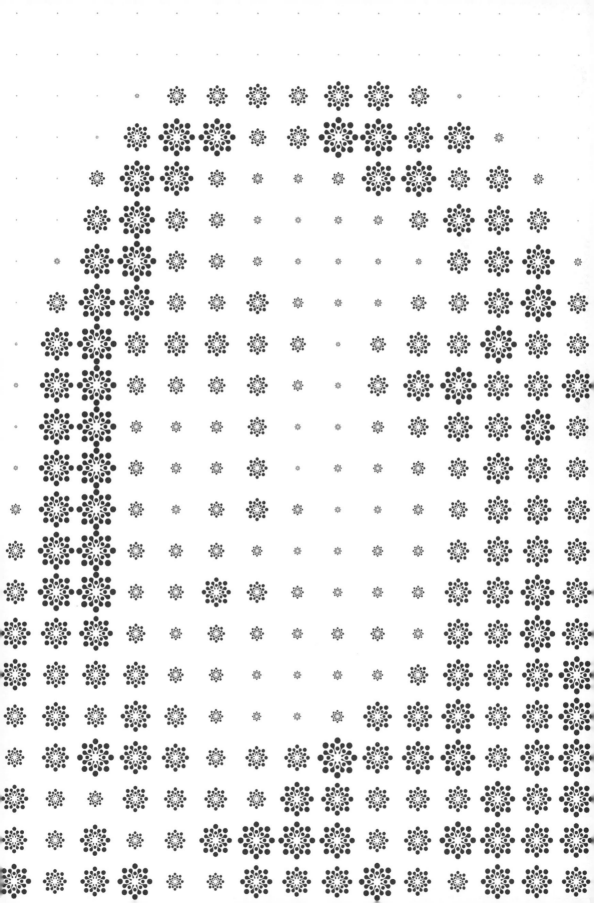

036

I was diagnosed with Essential Thrombocythaemia in 2015. I started feeling really poorly so saw Professor Harrison at Guys – she specialises in Myeloproliferative Neoplasms (MPN: a rare condition that affects the blood). A BMB confirmed Polycythaemia Vera iron deficient Jak 2, but it's not considered high risk. Within two weeks I had a heart attack caused by a blood clot from the MPN, which was a slow growing blood cancer. I was put on oral chemotherapy in July 2017 and still take it daily.

My perspective is that I am lucky to be alive but I live with daily fatigue, anxiety, depression, burning in my hands and feet, leg pain, chest pain and headaches. People always tell me 'I don't look ill'. On a good day I can be awesome, but inside I'm in agony. I have Fibromyalgia too and am breathless at times. My moods are erratic. Along with my emotions, forgetfulness is another issue from this disease and a side effect of the chemotherapy. Every day is a battle. I struggle with the disease, chemotherapy and hospital appointments. Plus, I always need to keep an eye on my body for changes. At the moment the disease is non-curable, so I may be on low dose chemotherapy for years to come.

Lots of friends do not understand and alienate themselves from me. Some are suffocating. None of us are invincible to this disease and we must at all times remain positive as this is part of our life plan. I find it hard to comprehend as I don't drink or smoke (but I do have a sweet tooth). No one else has this disease in my family.

Grace

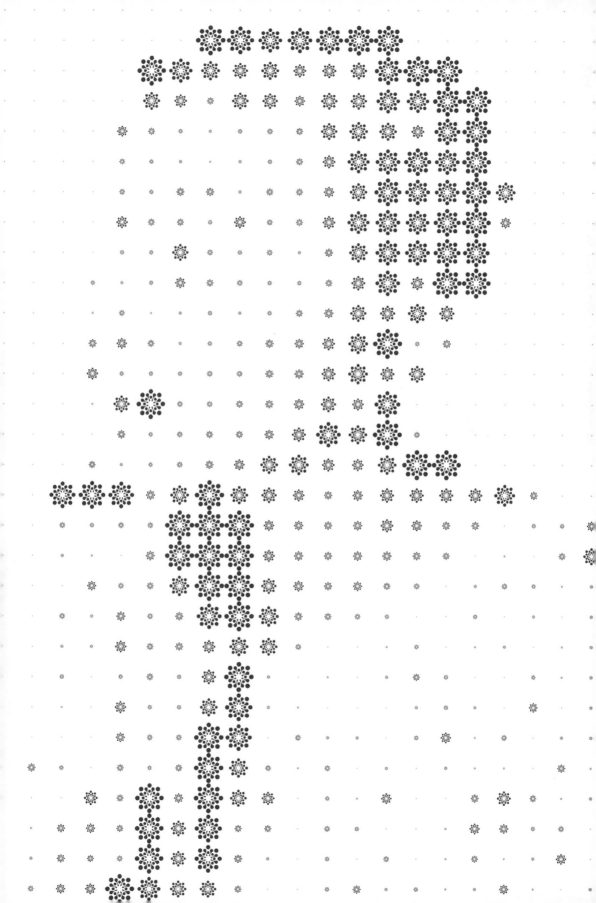

037

My brain tumour has changed my life, but probably not in the way you'd think. It's given me the most unique and positive perspective on life; I now know what matters most, which of my friends are worth keeping around, and how to value and make time for myself. I am no longer afraid to go after what I want – whether that's a small thing like a part time job in one of my favourite shops, or taking meetings with literary agents and saying yes to modelling underwear for a big, badass, body positive brand.

On the darker side, it's also meant I have had to adjust to living with a 'thing'. I now have to tick quite a few boxes on job applications, flight booking forms and MRI questionnaires. I have to be prepared to warn people about it, or try to casually drop it into conversation, and then have to tell them the full story over and over again. I'd say social media has massively helped with this; when I don't feel like telling everyone everything, they can just look through my older tweets or click through to the subcategory on my blog that will tell them all they need to know. I have found all kinds of support through groups on Facebook, hashtags on Instagram and weekly chats on Twitter. All those platforms have helped me be more open about my cancer, and I think openness generally is seriously important when it comes to this topic. It doesn't need to be so tricky to talk about.

Eleni

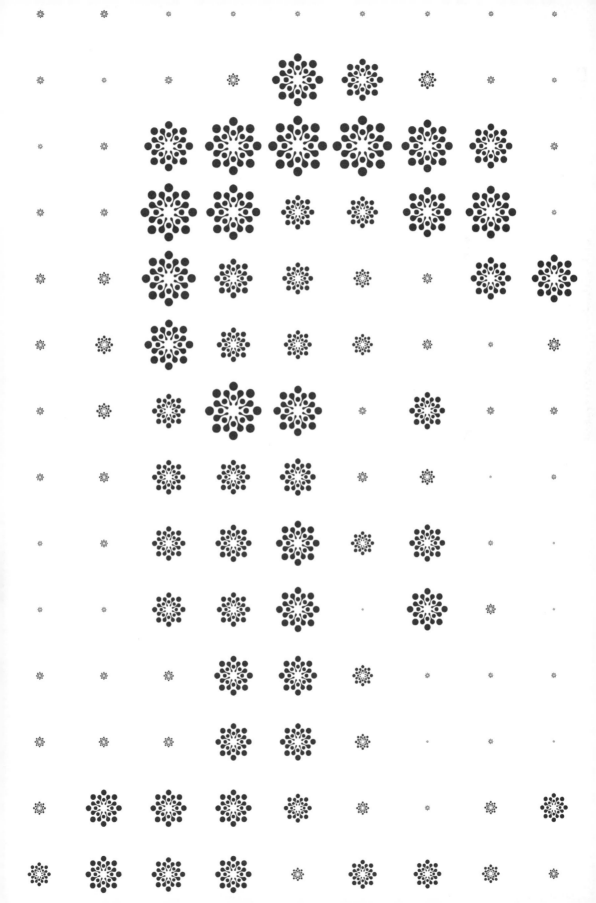

038

Cancer has completely changed me. I have two children and just soldiered through diagnosis and active treatment because what other choice did I have? But afterwards is a completely different story. I have days where I am positive and appreciative of life. I want to do and see everything possible to make my mark, but other days I am riddled with anxiety that affects my confidence and I just want to be alone.

I have friends that just won't talk about it. Some do, but you can tell they don't really want to. Everyone is so scared about knowing what to say or what they think they should say or what's right to say! It is part of most people's lives now and by normalising the conversation it will make people more comfortable. It will help people ask for and offer help and support in a more practical, positive way. Plus have a better understanding as to how each individual is feeling – be it patient, carer or family. Also, there are far more 'success' stories than 'worse case scenarios' but still the main thought when you hear the word cancer, is death.

I have found that social media, such as Instagram, has played a big part in me putting myself out there. 'A picture paints a thousand words' comes to mind and by showing the unfiltered me allows people to see what you're really going through. Also you connect with people you may not have done in your everyday life. I didn't find anyone in the groups I was sent to that were 'like me', but Instagram opened up a whole new support system that I had access to 24 hours a day.

Leanne

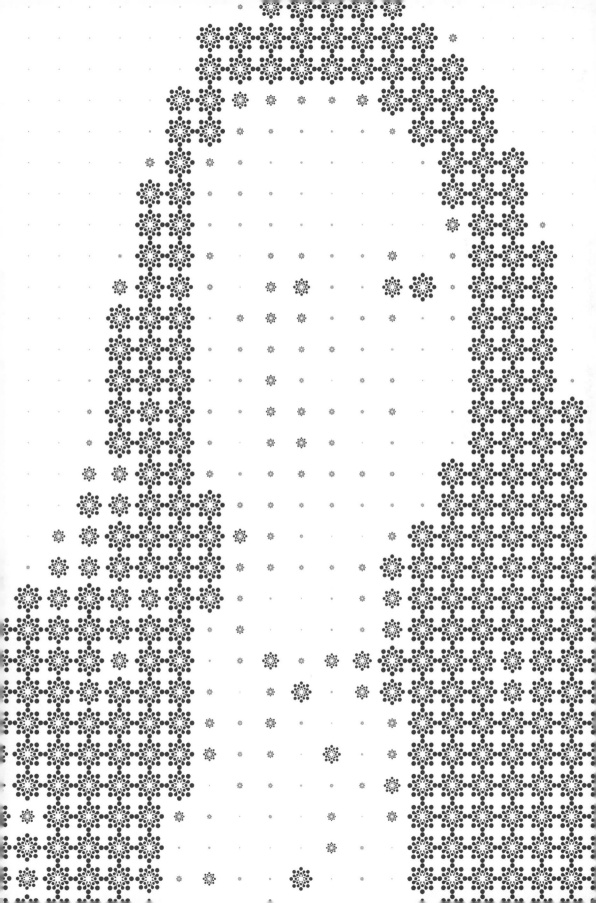

039

Cancer has made me feel every single emotion. I have felt numb, vulnerable, lonely, hurt, angry, empowered and scared. Cancer has taken a dream from me that I think about every single day and my heart feels broken. I am becoming more comfortable with my future, but I have fear in me of hearing those words again.

Open conversation is important for me because it is providing emotional and practical support. Having been avoided by some over my cancer diagnosis, it felt like a very lonely place and this was hard to understand why. Asking the person if they would like to spend some time together or to talk reaches out to the person and allows the person to decide what and how much they want to share. I understand people may not know what to say. Equally it is important to be honest with the person, because in saying that it leads the conversation.

The cancer community on social media has been a supportive and safe place for me to share my experiences, my feelings, the highs and the lows. I have connected with people that I wouldn't have on a normal day-to-day basis. I have been supported, but I too have supported people with their cancer. It feels very comfortable talking to someone who knows what it feels like to hear 'you have cancer' – it is a connection you have immediately but it is a connection that no one ever really wants to have. It is okay to have good and bad days, it is okay to have fears but knowing you can chat openly about those feelings is such a comfort to the individual.

Ben

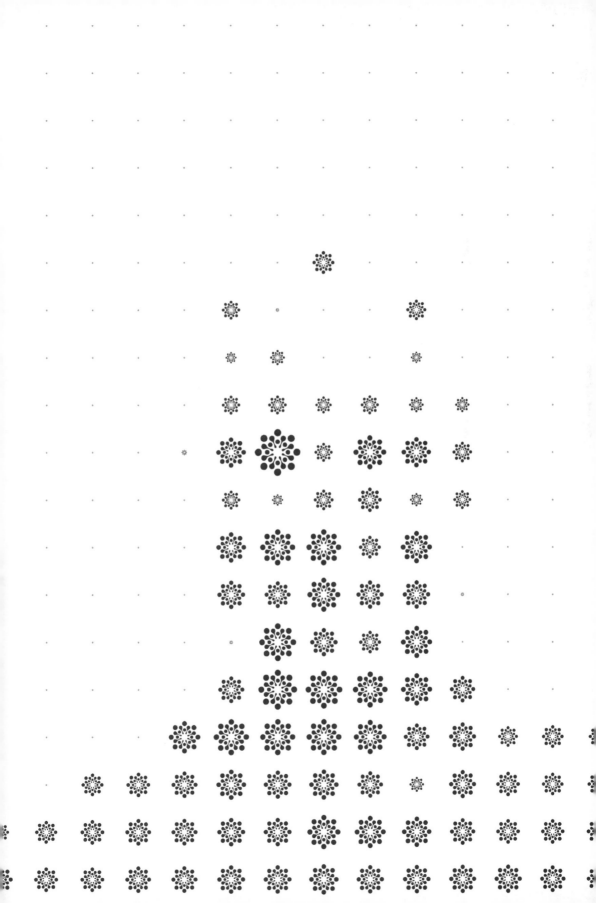

040

I was diagnosed with Hodgkin's Lymphoma in 2015. It has changed my life for the better. Yes, it was a horrendous time and I went through so much during my treatment – yet with hindsight I believe I was given a second opportunity to make a difference. Not just for my life but to make a difference to others.

The cancer allowed me to take stock of my life and review what was important to me. This has completely changed how I view life. I haven't changed in terms of how I hold myself, my personality is still similar, but it's the internal strength I now have. I feel like a completely different person. Talking about cancer is key, it shouldn't be viewed as a death sentence like it was 40 to 50 years ago. There is so much good research out there in regards to managing treatments and lifestyle. It's safe to say that people now are 'living with cancer'. By discussing their own approach and lifestyles, in person and on social media, this can help support others and inspire others to further understand.

Living with cancer still means I am human (I write this as past tense) I can still do things and achieve a lot. Although small understanding from others is key, as I might not be firing on all cylinders. People can be scared of what to say or do around friends with cancer, but I always wanted to be treated the same – treat me no differently, but respect that I might not be as fit or as sharp every day and not all days are the same.

Rebecca

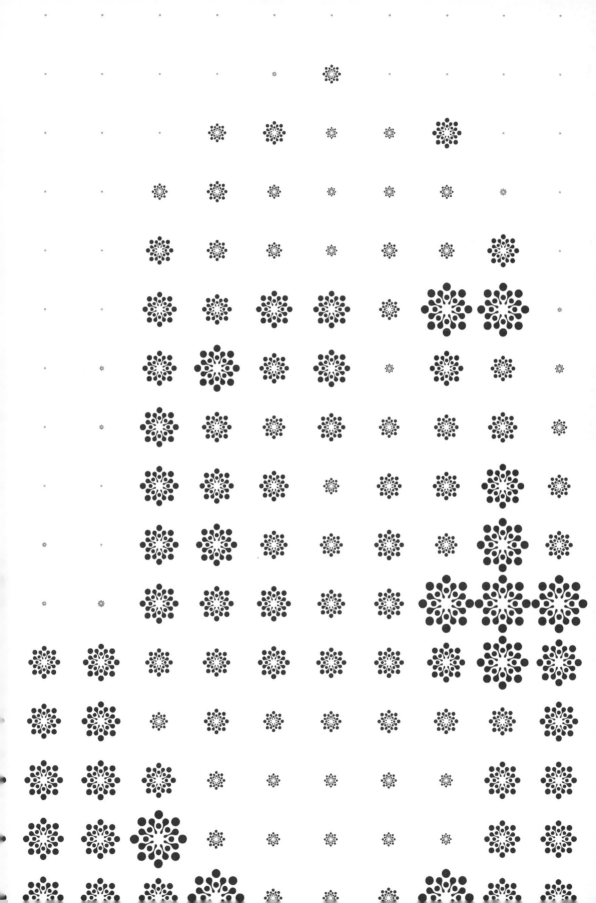

041

I was diagnosed with stage 3 bowel cancer at age 30. Because I was so young, despite having the 'obvious' symptoms that we all know as being associated with bowel cancer, it was a much delayed diagnosis. Meaning that by the time I had my surgery I was very unwell and unable to eat for 10 days post-op. This resulted in my weight dropping to six and a half stone. It took me months to regain the weight I had lost, with constant nausea and vomiting. Cancer 'rocks' our foundations; it made me question my will to go on and it took every ounce of energy I had left to keep going. It's the things that others don't see that got to me – the endless pain, nausea, vomiting, weakness and inability to 'carry on as before'.

Cancer is discussed much more than it has been in the past and yet there is still a long way to go. People often think that they can understand what cancer patients are going through when they get the diagnosis, but details such as stomas or losing an organ are often avoided. There is such a stigma around having a stoma and yet it is the best thing for me, I have my life back with it!

I never used Twitter prior to my diagnosis but I set up an account about eight months later. I found that I had a platform where I could discuss cancer and recovery related issues and there were helpful responses from cancer patients and medical staff. I believe that social media is breaking the barriers, so we are talking about topics that we wouldn't have been able to in the past.

Jacqui

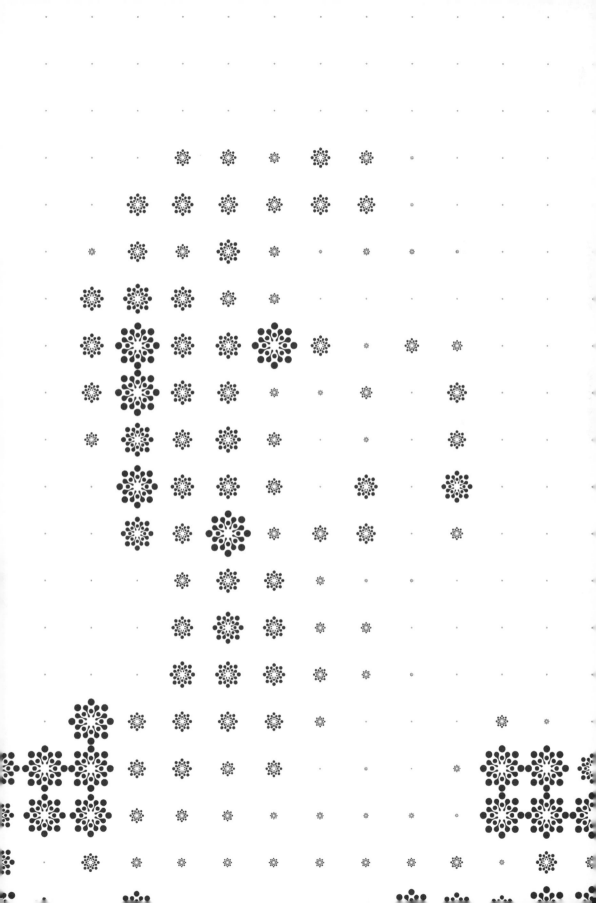

042

I was diagnosed with early stage breast cancer in December 2018. Having been through a lumpectomy and radiotherapy I still find the whole situation quite bizarre – almost like I don't feel as if I had cancer because I haven't felt unwell from it. I feel quite guilty that my cancer was so easy to deal with and has now gone, when so many have such a difficult time and don't always recover. The day of my diagnosis I then travelled 200 miles north, by train, to attend the funeral of a good friend of mine from pancreatic cancer. He didn't survive and I have. It leads to lots of questions of 'why?' in my head.

I am eternally grateful that I didn't need chemotherapy, it seems odd to say I feel fortunate when I have just had cancer – but I do. They found it early, they treated it and I am now clear of it. I do find that the minute you tell a friend or relative of the diagnosis they immediately get that look of horror. I found I was constantly reassuring them that I was and would be fine. Maybe more open discussions, that 'not all cancers destroys lives' would help. I've even managed to work through the majority of my treatment and maintain a reasonable sense of normality to my life – cancer did not take over. I have been more tired and needed to let others do more, but otherwise I have managed to remain incredibly positive throughout. I also realise how many other people having radiotherapy did not look ill and it made me wonder how many people you see walking around are coping with such massive issues without any signs to the outer world.

Lucy

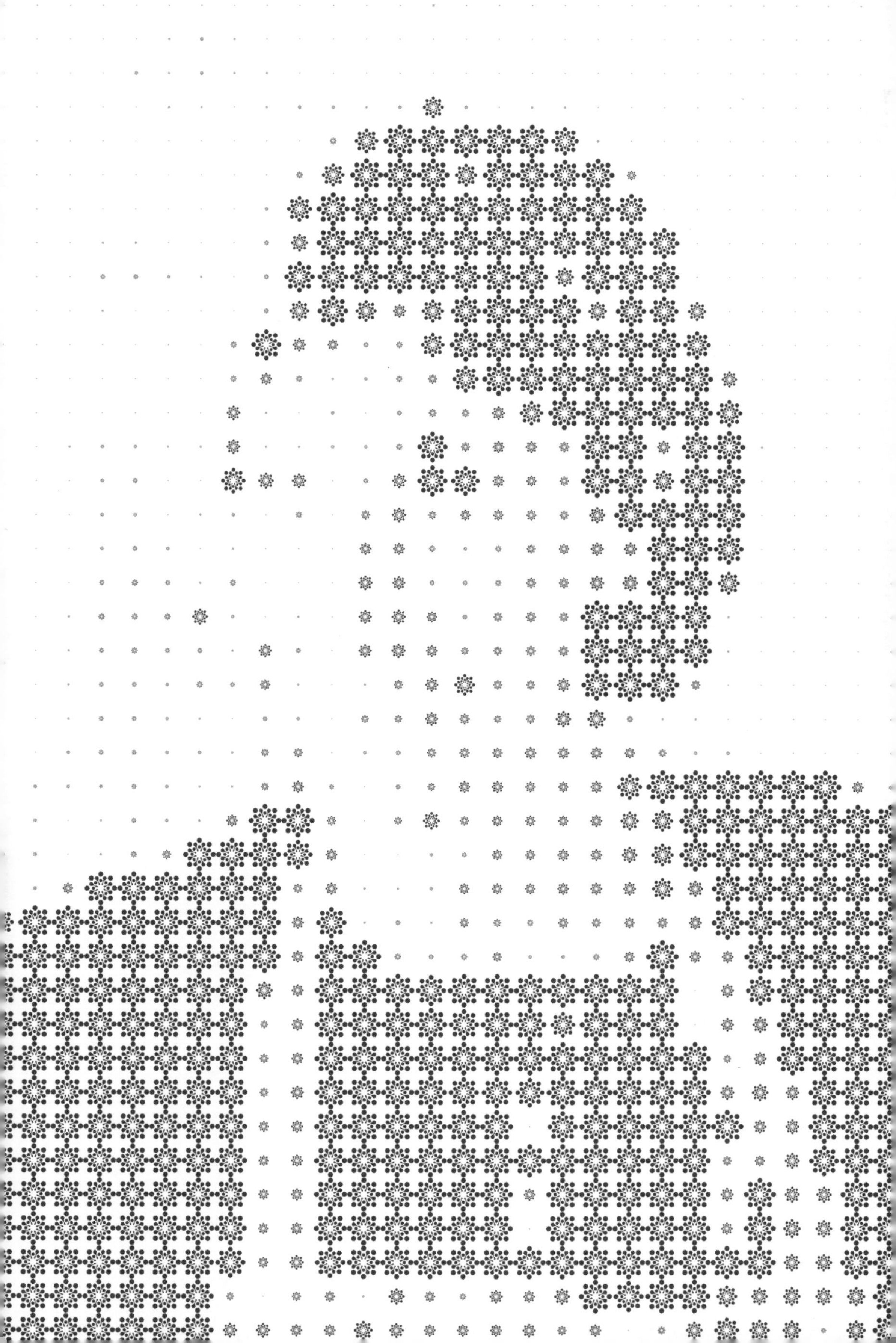

043

Here are the basics. I'm called Lucy, I'm married with two boys who are aged 11 and 13. I was diagnosed with Melanoma in 2011 and it progressed to stage 4 in September 2013. Despite being given months to live, I believe a combination of luck, access to drugs, being proactive and staying on top of my treatment, means I'm still here.

Cancer has given me my very worst day – the day I was told I had months not years and I had to face my absolute terror about not seeing my boys grow up. Oddly, perhaps because I have been fortunate with treatment and the months have in fact turned into years I have probably laughed more than I've cried over the last five and a half years. I live a much better life, with less complacency. I just wish the cancer would go away now!

I think people are very fearful of talking about cancer – even the word is difficult for many people. Hand in hand with that is the fear of talking about dying and that, for me, has been much more problematic. I end up not being able to be honest about my fears and often gloss over what I'm actually feeling. I have tried my best to teach my boys not to fear the word but to understand that cancer is not just one thing – there are many types, it affects people in different ways, treatments are different and it doesn't always lead to death.

I think Twitter, in particular, is very useful for connecting with other people who are experiencing similar issues in terms of their diagnosis. I also hope that the frank honest discussions that take place between various people with cancer on Twitter helps to educate everyone.

Victoria

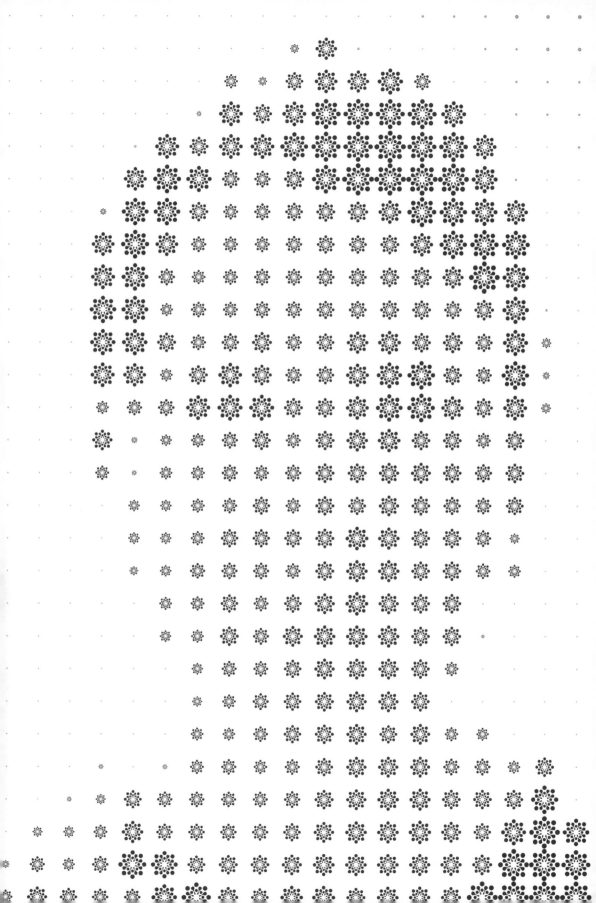

044

Most significantly cancer affected my life when my mum died when I was just age 22. She was 47 years old. It has affected me in different ways during my life but I feel the loss more now as an adult, wife and mother. I have also had friends that have had cancer and survived, but also friends that have died.

Cancer also now affects me on a professional level. I work as an Art Therapist at Maggie's Cambridge. The reasons why we should talk about cancer are lengthy but ultimately it needs to be talked about to stop the taboo's. One in two of us will get cancer, it needs to be a conversation that we are not afraid to have.

If you have cancer you need to be able to talk to people openly about how you feel – the good, the bad, and the ugly. You need a support network and if those around you are afraid to talk about cancer they will be unable to support you or won't know how to support you. We need to be more open about conversations that involve death and dying so that we can ultimately start to have conversations about living with cancer.

I am on the fence with social media. I think that it allows people with cancer to have a network of people and information when they need to find it. However, I believe that we are unable to process the issues that are faced when given a cancer diagnosis unless you have a real life community, with real life relationships. Because we, as human beings, are inescapably social creatures. People may need to seek out new relationships and communities when a cancer diagnosis comes along but ultimately we need physical, present, face-to-face support.

Nichola

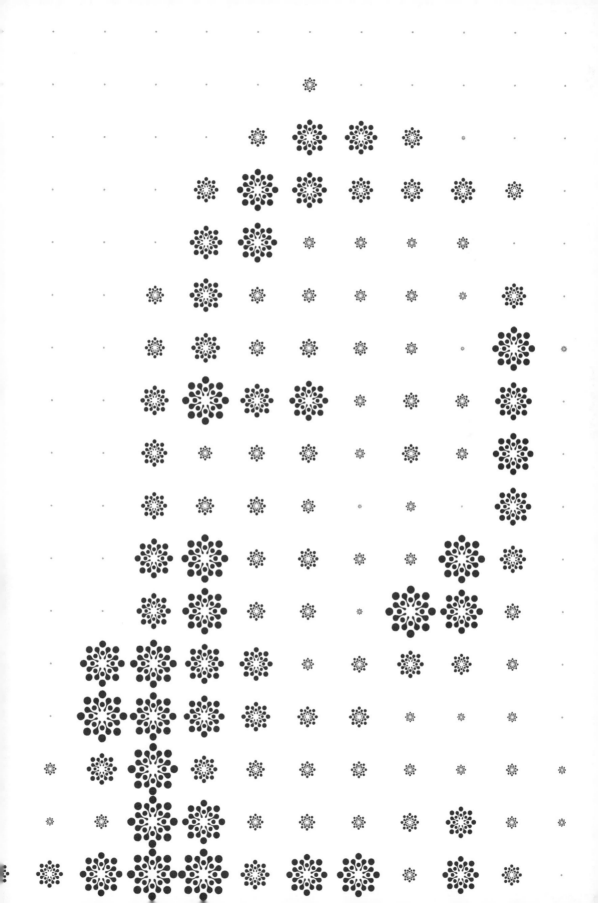

045

Cancer has been life changing, and not in a good way. I have become more anxious, more depressed and my body has changed inside and out. When you are diagnosed, you never realise what you are about to embark on. I just thought I'd have the operation and that would be it. But it feels like as soon as you have your head round one thing, another hits you. Dealing with early menopause and weakened bones are the most recent things, on a long list.

I think more needs to be done, especially with regard to the long lasting effects. Many people don't understand that you will never be back to the 'normal' you were, and think that once you are over the operation and chemotherapy you will be okay again. Whereas I don't feel I'll ever be who I was before cancer and that can be hard to come to terms with. Workplaces need to have a better appreciation of this, as that has also proved difficult for me. People shouldn't be afraid to say they are struggling, and others should also be more aware of this without having to be told. That's why I think the more open discussion the better.

Through social media I have been fortunate enough to meet and become a part of a wider community, who all know instinctively how I feel and what I am going through. This support has become invaluable. I am also part of the #truecancerbodies movement which was recently set up on Instagram. The movement tries to get past the unrealistic brand campaigns we see for cancer charities to find more realistic ways of raising awareness that us sufferers can relate to. Social media and the internet have opened my eyes to a whole new world of mutual understanding and the chance to make a positive difference.

Tracey

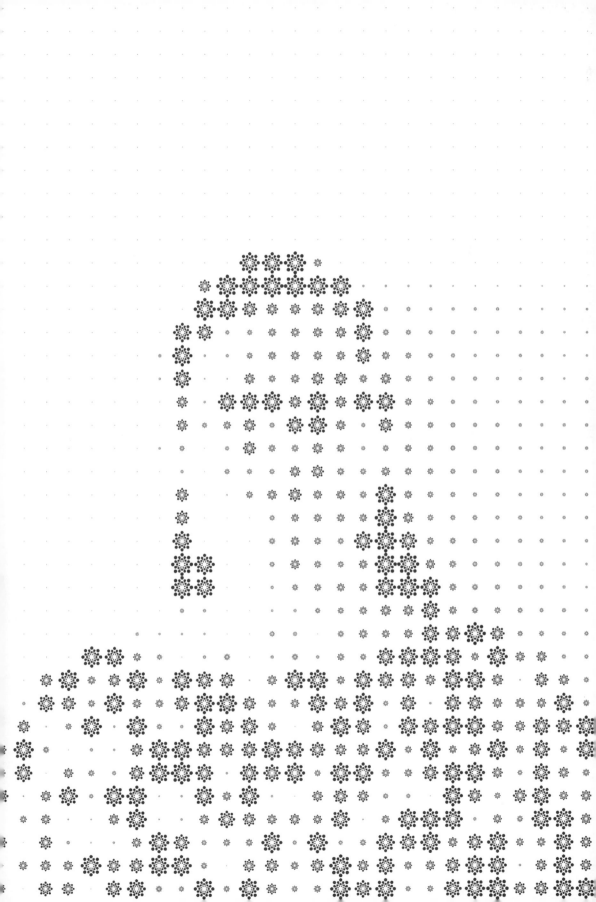

046

I lost my husband, Steve, to Leukaemia 23 years ago, he was 34 years old. 10 years ago, when I was age 41, I found out I had thyroid cancer and five years ago I was diagnosed with Leiomyiosarcoma, a soft tissue tumour of the bladder.

I wish I was able to talk more openly about cancer. When my husband was diagnosed in 1992, most people would use the phrase 'the Big-C' rather than utter the word cancer. So things have improved in some way, but for me I still feel there is a shame attached to the disease. I have definitely missed out on advice and support due to my reluctance to 'share' my experience and own diagnosis. I now know, looking back, that I have struggled with my own mental health because I was unable to access any help groups or to accept support from friends and family due to mine and societies reluctance to share and talk openly about cancer.

Social media has certainly helped me share my experiences. I am generally sharing my own diagnosis with strangers, people who know nothing about me and this has helped me. The internet has also helped bring cancer into the open, opening up discussions, actively encouraging people to share their experiences and in turn we are giving each other hope and advice. We need to normalise cancer, as it is a disease that scares many, many people. People are scared as soon as they hear the word and when they are diagnosed. People lower their voices when speaking the word cancer. From my own experiences, I know that it can be a lonely journey, I wasn't able to speak openly about my cancers as I feared upsetting people – worried that I would make people feel awkward or uncomfortable. We need to make it so that no one faces cancer alone, because of fear of sharing. Normalising cancer would benefit many.

Alison

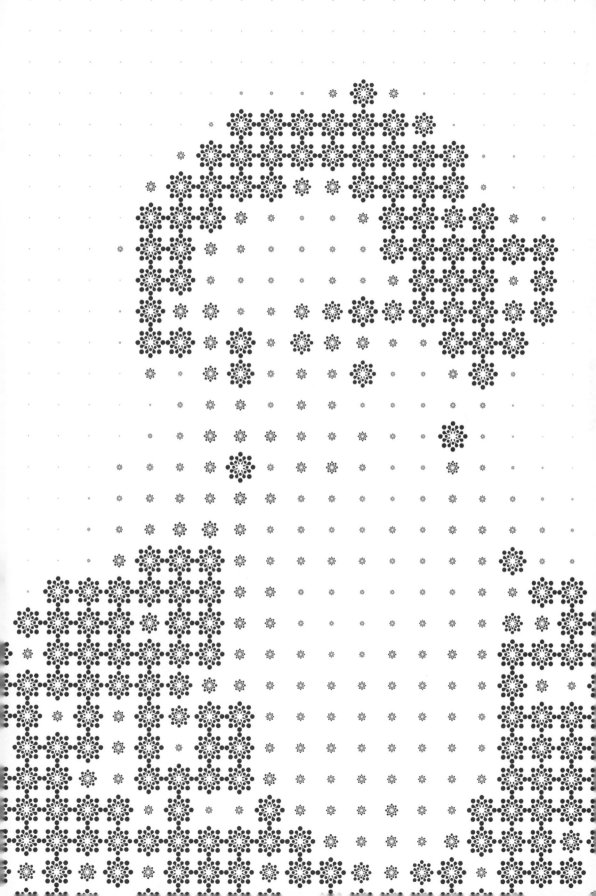

047

My mum had breast cancer (separate cancers in both breasts) and died aged 37 when I was four. I have always had the worry that I was at higher risk and I found a lump a month before my 32nd birthday. During my chemotherapy my dad was diagnosed with lymphoma and he started treatment just as I finished mine.

The public perception of cancer is so skewed by adverts and campaigns but nobody understands exactly what it all involves, so open discussions are needed. Everyone's cancer treatment is different, but the media depictions make the process even harder. Adverts for charities show treatment as throwing up and losing hair – then being full of energy and excited when treatment is over. For me chemotherapy was horrid but mentally I felt better during chemotherapy than I have since my active treatment ended. I finished chemotherapy over a year ago (then had a double mastectomy and reconstruction) but I am still suffering with side effects. My treatment hasn't ended (I still have around nine more years of hormone treatment to go), yet as soon as my hair grew back everyone assumed I was back to normal.

I have been sharing parts of my story on social media, as it is my life now. I try to explain how and why things are happening and explain the surprising things. I have had comments from people saying they have found it so interesting to learn the things I share. I have tried to give support to people, as the online world has been so supportive to me during treatment – either people I already knew that I can communicate with while stuck at home, or people on cancer support groups. Open discussion is important so people can share what cancer is really like, as it will help people feel less alone and help family and friends say and do the most supportive things.

Vicky

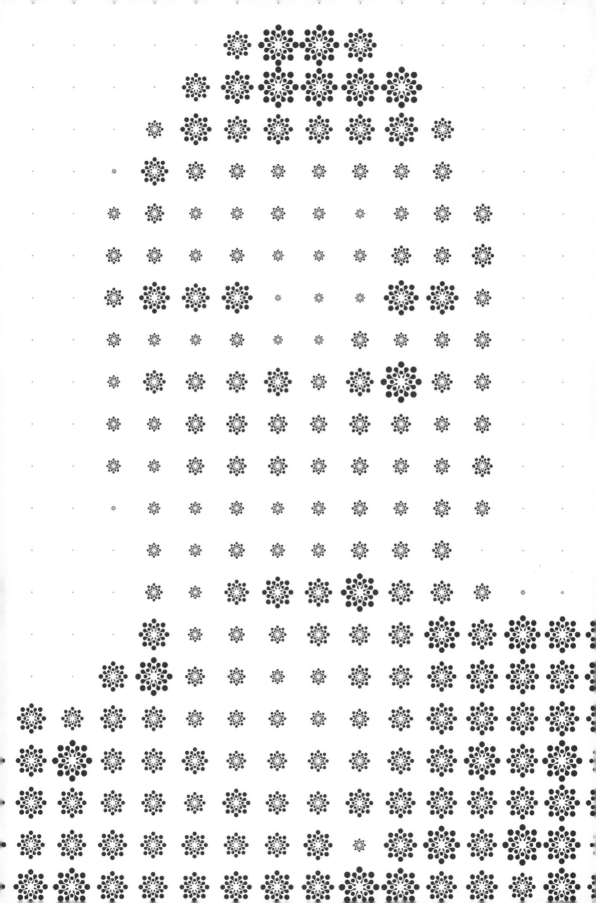

048

Without question, cancer has changed me – but for the better. I no longer take things for granted, and I no longer sweat the small stuff. I am grateful to my body for getting me through the brutality of treatment and have a newfound respect for it. I'm grateful for small everyday things I never noticed before.

Cancer is scary and was once a disease you died of, if you got it. It's a disease people are afraid of, and afraid to talk about. The older generations have a very different view of cancer and treatment to today's generation. Today you can be treated successfully. However as a nation we are not body aware and body responsible, and early detection of cancer saves lives. If we discuss symptoms more openly, then more people will be treated earlier. It's also so important to educate people on the reality of cancer. I was so shocked when I met many young women with breast or bowel cancer. People think it only happens to you when you're old, or you're unlucky. Sadly that's not the case anymore. Normalising the discussion will encourage people to get help earlier, and not feel so alone if they do get diagnosed.

My only support came from social media. The majority of my friends chose to say nothing, as they were too scared to say the wrong thing or 'didn't know what to say'. Suddenly you become alienated from people you know as once you're diagnosed and going through active treatment, your world is taken over by symptoms, side effects, drugs and cancer. Social media helps connect you with people that are going through the exact same crisis as you. So that understanding and support is invaluable. That's why I founded True Cancer Bodies – it's a safe place to meet other cancer patients and get the support you need.

Mark

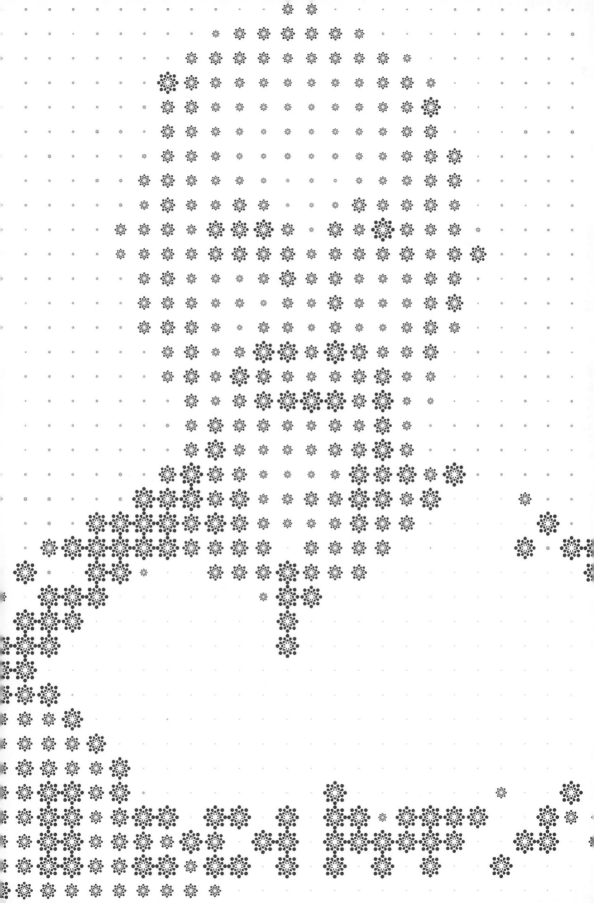

049

Upon diagnosis, obviously I felt like my life was turned upside down, I was worried how it would affect my family (my son, Oliver, was only nine years old). I was also dealing with my Dad having bowel cancer at the same time, who sadly passed away while I was ill. I had to give up my job for two years, as the treatment made me so poorly. I was barely able to walk. So financially it affected us too. There are so many things you have to deal with – like filling forms in, going for interviews to check you are 'really' ill – when all you should have to do is manage the treatment and hopefully get well. My Dad kept his symptoms to himself, and upon diagnosis still didn't talk about it. I vowed if ever I got ill (little did I know it was only round the corner) I wouldn't do that to my family. I also found going to a local cancer support group Bloodbuddies is very helpful (I still go), as we have all been or are going through it so can help each other by talking about our experiences.

I took up cycling for my recovery and I honestly feel it's given me my life back. I wear my Blood Cancer (#cyclingtobeatmybloodcancer) top with pride and it's amazing how many people stop me and ask if I'm raising money for blood cancer and then I can share with them my experience and how cycling has given me a fantastic boost to my wellbeing.

I had never used social media until I started doing charity cycle rides, it has been an amazing help to raise funds and awareness and to get in touch with other people fighting the same illness. It has also enabled me to meet with people from Bloodwise and other blood cancer charities. I joined Bloodwise through social media and had a fantastic experience cycling the London to Paris charity ride in 2015.

Louise

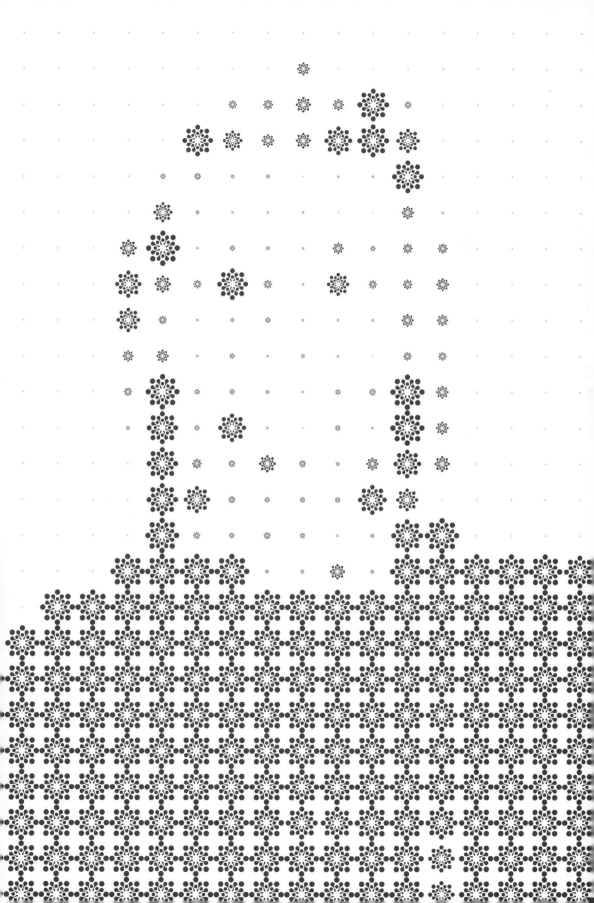

050

I think one of the biggest effects of cancer is actually once the treatment has finished. Once I returned to work, it was clear that people thought my life was back to normal but after a cancer diagnosis, life is never the same again. I call it the 'new normal'. I appreciate life more, my friends and family more but I am also acutely aware of my own mortality. Of course we are all going to die but when you are diagnosed at a relatively early age that is brought home to you. You do move on, and I am now two years in remission which means that cancer is no longer the first thing I think about when I wake up in the morning or the last thing I think about when I go to bed at night. But it's always there now – like a shadow – and the important thing is not to let that affect your future.

I think it's great that so much has been done to normalise cancer and the conversations surrounding it. A lot of that has been done through social media and role models. When I was growing up, cancer was something that happened to old people – or so it seemed. Now, barriers have been broken down and it's clear that cancer doesn't discriminate – it affects young and old, white, black, Asian, male and female. Speaking about it more and seeing people living well – despite a cancer diagnosis – is really important in normalising cancer.

I think social media has really helped raise awareness of the fact that younger people also get cancer. It has enabled people with cancer to build strong communities in a way they wouldn't have been able to before. It has also encouraged people to be honest about their cancer, about the way they look, or feel and it means you can see other people like you going through cancer – which means you don't feel so alone.

Clodagh

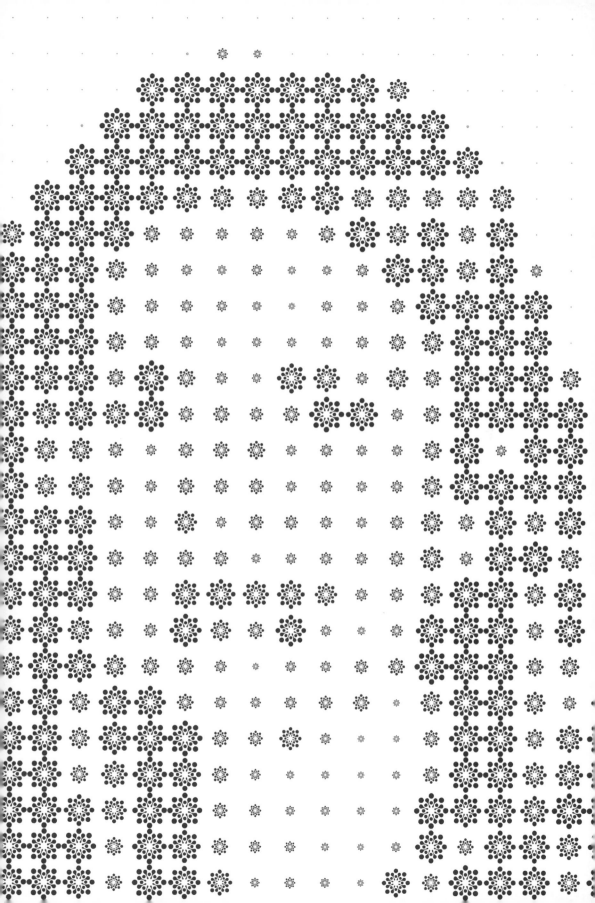

051

Obviously, no one would choose to have cancer, but I have to say that it has enriched my life. I am more appreciative of simple things. I am very thankful for birthday's and I have made some great friends, whom I would never have met outside the cancer space. I also feel I am a better doctor for having been a patient. Oh, and I'm now an avid dragon boater! I helped found a club locally, made up predominantly of ladies who have had a diagnosis of breast cancer. It's a great outlet on so many levels.

Conversations about having cancer have become so much more mainstream since I was a child, when it was pretty taboo. At least part of the reason for this is that cancer treatment has progressed so much. There are many more people who have survived cancer or are living with a cancer diagnosis. Being able to have open conversations about cancer (including fears for the future, as well as discussions about experience of cancer treatment) is obviously important for the people with cancer but also very helpful for the people around them and indeed for all of society as one in two of us will get cancer at some stage.

Social media conversations allow people to talk about cancer with other people in a similar situation, without necessarily burdening friends or family with their fears. It also allows people who have not had cancer to find out more about the experience. I feel it 'normalises' having cancer. I think Rachel Bland and the 'You, Me & the Big C' podcast team have made a huge difference in this respect – young, glam women talking about the nitty gritty of the disease, even in the face of death, has opened the public's eyes to the fact that anyone is susceptible. I feel the broader conversations about mortality are also extremely helpful to society, and obviously applicable to more diseases than cancer.

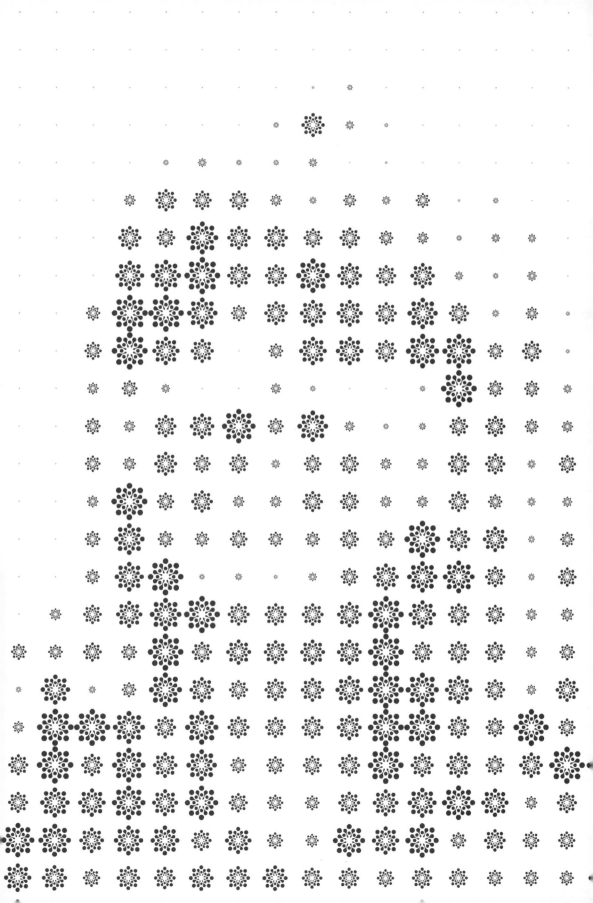

052

I always thought that if I was unlucky to be diagnosed with cancer, that it would destroy me. Now being diagnosed with terminal cancer I have found that isn't the case. Cancer has made me stronger than ever. I am more confident because I am aware that I don't have the time to grow into who I am meant to be. It has opened up my life to so many wonderful things – I have done so much, that I wouldn't have done otherwise. I have spoken at The Houses of Parliament, at the 'All-Party Parliamentary Group on Cancers' Conference. Spreading awareness of this evil disease has given me a new purpose and, of course, I have met so many amazing, wonderful people.

We all need to be much more open and honest about how we feel going through treatment. We need to show that there is a real downside, a side that doesn't seem to deal with emotional issues once your treatment has stopped. We are left to deal with so much, emotionally, and by being open we connect with others. We share our hopes, our dreams and our fears for the future. By doing this we allow ourselves to be real and we realise, most importantly, that we are not alone, regardless of what cancer we have and that there is always hope and love.

Social media allows us to connect with those going through the same thing as us, it allows us to engage with others, support and comfort others, as well as being able to support and comfort ourselves during those dark days. It allows us to see that we aren't alone on this shitty journey, we can laugh, have honest conversations, conversations that we may not want to have with our families or friends but to those who know exactly how we feel. We can share stories of courage and despair and feel like we belong.

Jenny

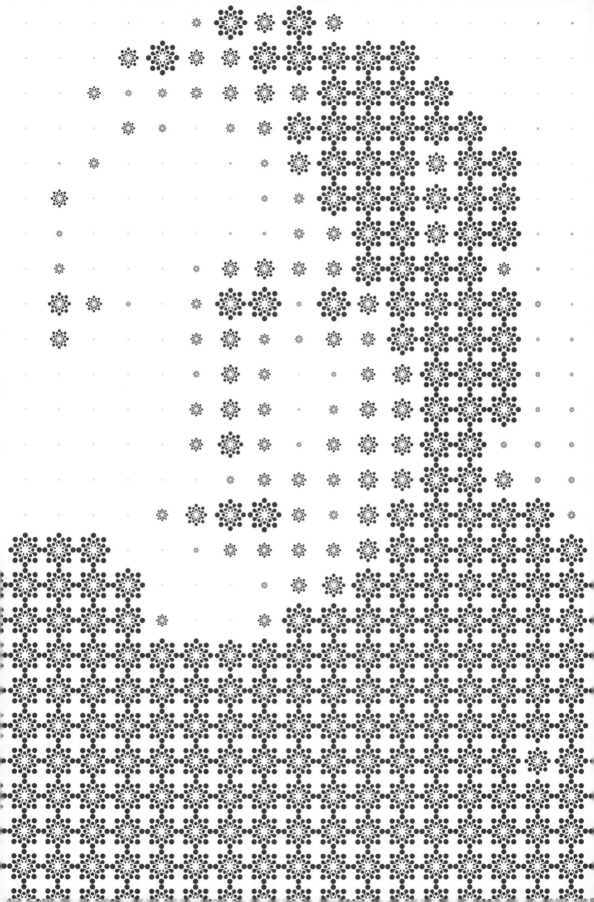

053

I am still processing everything that happened. Some days I feel almost normal, and others it is like having someone else's hangover, combined with the worst jet lag (insomnia, drowsiness and general confusion) plus post gym aches – the same pain and stiffness you get when you've not been spinning regularly and you've seriously over done it (I try to use everyday comparisons as it makes it all less scary). Telling people is still the hardest thing for me. I dread having 'The Conversation', so if people know about my diagnosis it just makes everything easier. It prevents misunderstandings and fear. My friends know that I might need to cancel plans and my boss understands when I need more time to complete assignments. If people did not know, I worry they would think me lazy, distant or flakey. It has got easier. When I was first diagnosed, I could not say the sentence 'I have cancer' without crying. Now it feels odd, but I can get the words out without tears. So, talking more makes these conversations better in some way.

Talking also serves to demystify cancer. I have heard so many times 'You don't look like a cancer patient; you look so healthy'. I take this as a compliment, but it shows that there is an assumption of how the illness must change everyone. I have learnt that cancer is such an individual experience, everyone responds differently. As a result, I like the idea of wearing a 'Cancer On board' badge when travelling by public transport as my disability is hidden and I feel weird claiming a seat.

I would not have heard about this project if it were not for Twitter! Overall, social media has helped maintain connections with the outside world. I attend a local support centre (Cancer Care) but for the times when I am feeling too weak etc, the centre has an online forum (Phoenix Group). It helps me to read about how others have had 'The Conversation'.

Angela

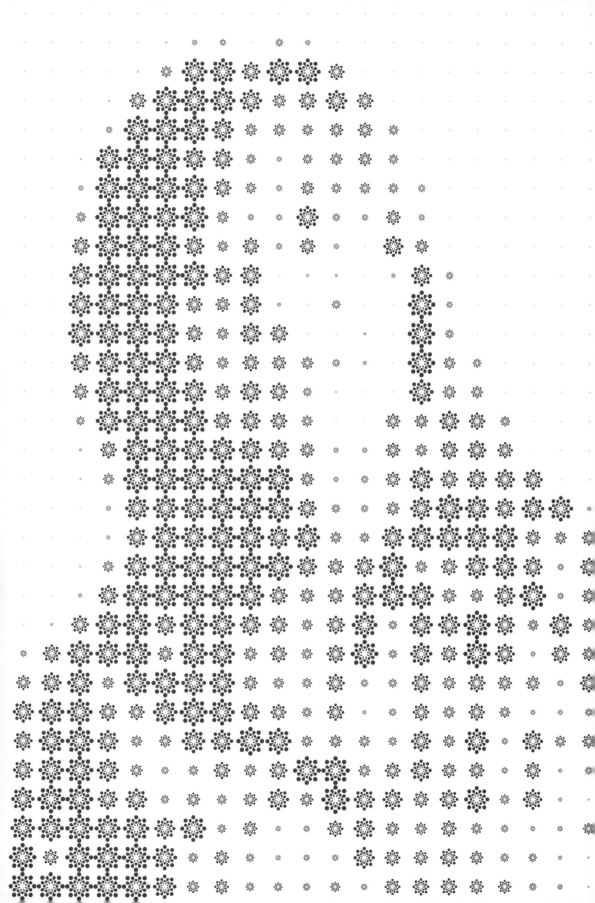

054

I was told that they thought it was cancer four days before Christmas. I was just going out to my Christmas party at work. I just couldn't take it in. I didn't feel ill, I didn't look ill. The little symptoms I had were, what I thought, due to previous surgery. I felt numb. I didn't understand. I cried a lot. I didn't sleep. It lay there, in my mind, all over Christmas. It was confirmed by a phone call on the 27th December 2018. 'Yes, it is cancer'. Boom, and there it was. Appointments, surgery, recovery and now chemotherapy.

It has had an effect of (1) fear of what I have already experienced, (2) anxiety of what is to come and (3) loss of the life I once had. The life I will never have anymore, because it will never leave me – it's there embedded in my head.

When I was diagnosed with cancer, it was a really scary time. It brings with it a fear of dying. When you're in hospital or with health professionals, it feels less frightening as they are so used to talking about it and treating it. But when you are outside of that, people are sad for you and they don't know what to say. It can be lonely. However, knowing that there are so many other people who are going through the same thing as you really helps. People avoid going to screenings because of fear and not knowing enough about it. Most people think they feel well and don't think it will happen to them – they don't realise you can have little or no symptoms. Changing our perception can lessen the fear. Open discussion can change the way we feel and help normalise the conversation. This will continue to raise awareness so people can be diagnosed earlier and have a better chance of survival.

Through social media I have embraced communities, shared experiences, talked to people, made friends, supported others and others have supported me. It has become a big part of the cancer conversation. The downside of the internet is 'googling', so I suggest it's best to keep away.

Lucy

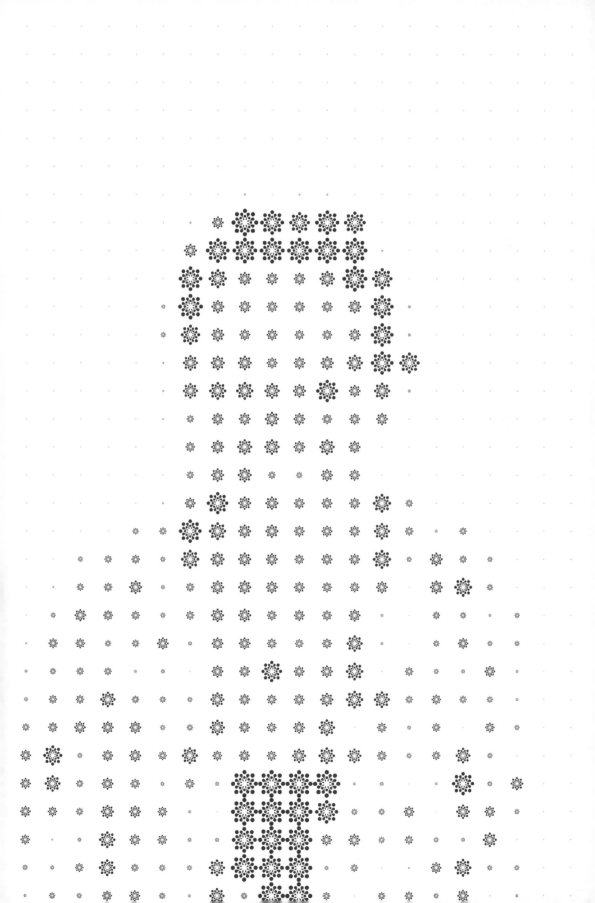

055

Cancer has affected me. I now remind myself that I don't really know what people are going through, or what they might have gone through already, so I am more sensitive towards others. Being 18 and being diagnosed is the last thing I thought would ever happen, so it's also a reminder that these things do happen, and they can happen to anyone. Cancer has made me realise that you're always going to have up and down days but when you're feeling good, you should make the most of it. Do things that make you happy and surround yourself with people who make you laugh.

When you hear about cancer it is usually connected to scary facts in the news or alongside fancy words that no one understands – so the conversation with cancer is limited. People are scared and don't want to engage in the disease but that just means that they know less about it. By trying to normalise the discussion it makes it less scary. The more people who understand cancer, the more they are educated and know what to look out for. When I was diagnosed, I had never heard of Lymphoma before, let alone know what the symptoms were and the forms of treatment. My friends were the same, so I had to do a lot of explaining. But explaining something which I didn't know much about. If this conversation is normalised, people will be able to understand and support others better.

Cancer is such an isolating experience, no matter how amazing your family and friends are, because you will always feel a little alone. Every single cancer diagnosis is so specific to you and your body. With the internet and social media that isolation decreases massively, by being able to connect with so many different people and hearing different experiences prepares you for what you might feel or think before it happens. It gives you reassurance that even though this diagnosis is so specific to you, there are many people out there that can simply relate and understand different aspects of how you're feeling and what you're really going through.

056

To be honest, I can't remember a time when cancer wasn't part of my life. I was eight at diagnosis, and 22 now, so I've been living in remission longer than I lived pre-cancer. I had Ewing's sarcoma which is a type of Bone Cancer, and my treatment included a full knee replacement. The impact of that led to about ten years of intermittent surgeries on my legs. This was the biggest physical impact cancer had on me, and meant I had mobility issues throughout my teenage years.

Despite this, the main way cancer has affected me is mentally/emotionally. Remission life comes with a lot of its own issues that are not talked about very much. For me, this led to chronic depression and anxiety.

I believe open conversation is the best catalyst for change. As people, we are beginning to normalise many 'taboo' subjects now, which shines real light onto different issues and makes us think about how we can solve them, all from just starting a conversation. Cancer is an especially hard topic because many of us have been so deeply affected – whether you're a patient, or a bereaved individual – emotions run high around this word. If everyone started talking about it more openly and honestly, we can pinpoint issues and solve them. Even if the issue is just feeling like you're all alone, by discussing it this reassures you that there are other people experiencing the same thing. This conversation can make real change.

The internet and social media have allowed us all to become authors. We can now write whatever we want, or even film ourselves saying it. It's out there for the world to see and respond to. This means we have an infinitely greater chance of speaking to someone going through the same thing – which has really helped to open the conversation about cancer. Especially for rare cancers, as the likelihood of knowing anyone in your circle or area with the same diagnosis is so low. I think this is one of the best uses for social media.

Dorothy

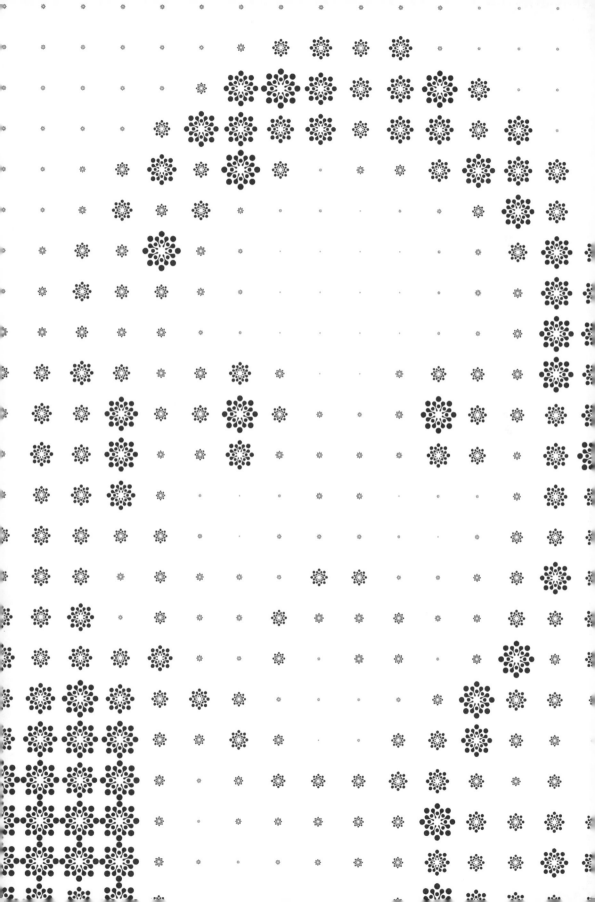

057

I always knew that life was short. My dad was shot dead in The Troubles, just before my sixth birthday. So, for the most part, I lived my life on that basis. When I was diagnosed at 44 with triple negative breast cancer, I just wanted to die quickly and have it over. A very close friend had died after an epic six-year struggle with cancer, so I saw up close how it could go. A huge moment for me was when the medics told me that I wouldn't die in pain. Then, I gradually began to realise that I might survive to see my boys grow up. Treatment has gone really well and I'm getting back on my feet. I have three precious boys and an amazing husband, and I want to hold them close. I also have a new puppy – she and I form a very powerful girl gang in the house and look forward to the future.

I found I didn't have the capacity to tell different people different things about my cancer, so it was easier not to waste energy covering it up. I have a wonderful group of coffee buddies and meeting up was both a distraction and a huge support. I let girlfriends feel the lump in my breast so they would know what to watch for. I think the younger generation are past the point of whispering about cancer. It is not the automatic death sentence that it once was. I have been given so much hope from other women a couple of years down the road from me and I feel I owe it to those just starting out on this road, to let them know there is hope.

WhatsApp was great for keeping people up to date, but it did bring a pressure to communicate when I hadn't processed a development myself or when I was exhausted. The internet was a source of both terrifying and invaluable information and had to be treated with caution. A wrong click could lead to despair for the rest of the day.

Elena

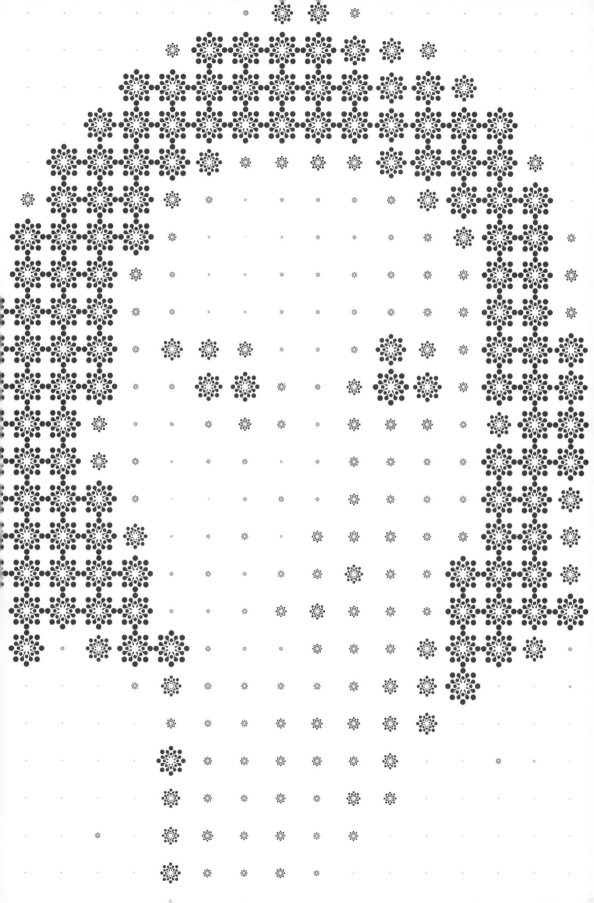

058

I was diagnosed and operated on over three years ago. I had a brain tumour (a low grade one) and although my tumour was a benign tumour, I still felt incredibly vulnerable and frightened. I spent the two weeks prior to surgery worrying about it. What if it didn't go to plan? A delicate surgery could affect my life emotionally, mentally and physically. After all I had been a ballet dancer for the last 20 years of my life. But, most importantly, how my diagnosis could have affected my immediate family. It was at this point that I realised how much I took my body awareness for granted. I cannot reiterate enough how important it is to listen to your mind and your body. It might be a very simple, obvious advice but again, far too often, we take it for granted.

My advice to anyone who has been affected by this terrible illness directly or even indirectly is to not ignore your worries, your doubt, or your fears. Not every ache or pain leads to something life threatening but you will never know unless you start investigating.

Talking about cancer, or any life-threatening physical condition is extremely important as it gives anyone a sense of closure, familiarity and reassurance. I am strong believer that when confronted with something frightening, we should face it. Confront it in the best possible way, even just a little chat with a close friend to express our fears and insecurities or seeking advice from a professional, is a step in the right direction.

I found social media and the internet very interesting and helpful at the same time. At times a bit too addicting, as I was constantly chatting with brain tumour groups on Facebook in order to seek advice and reassurance. But, most of the time, very helpful for obvious reasons. Any doubts were cleared, most questions answered and if at any point I felt low or sad I knew that I wasn't the only one going through a tough time. There was always someone somewhere that knew exactly how I felt, having gone through a similar journey.

Liz

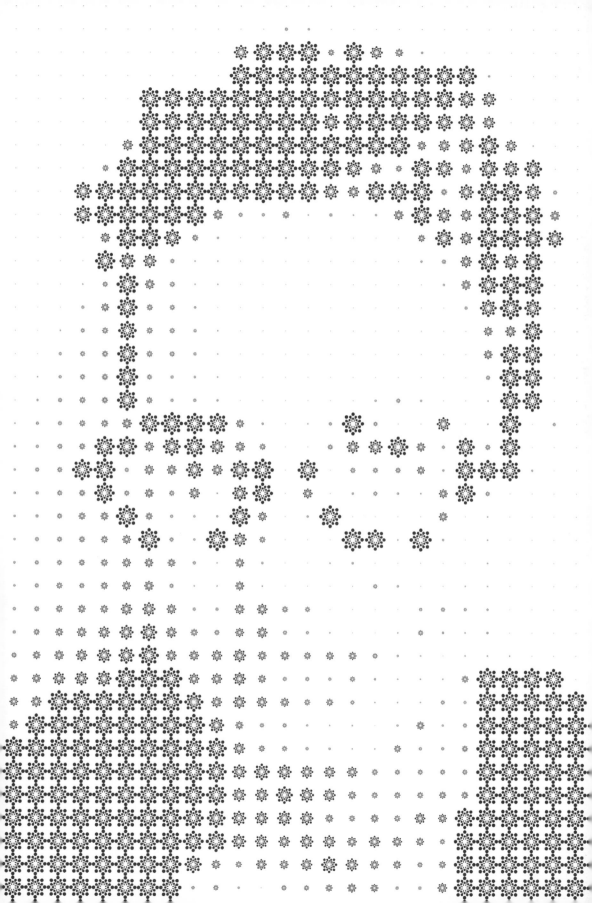

059

Cancer changed my world completely:

Physically – chemotherapy curls and life as a uni-boober with ugly scars on my chest wall.
Mentally – dealing with the depression and anxiety of a cancer diagnosis, and again when it came back. It's a bit like grieving – for what has happened to you, as well as the things that never will – such as infertility.
My identity as a woman – how to you find your femininity when you've lost your hair, your breasts, your ovaries and your sex hormones?
My job – I had to retire as a consultant breast surgeon because side effects of radiotherapy mean that I can no longer move my left arm properly, so I can't operate any more.

1 in 2 people will get cancer. It's no longer a disease of the elderly. We need to make it a normal word in everyday conversation. Take the fear, the shame and the guilt away. Teach people how to react to someone who has cancer – what to say, what not to say, how to help them. We also need to help cancer patients find others like them to get the support that they can't get from friends and family who don't have cancer. That's where online forums and social media have a huge part to play.

I told Twitter the day after I was diagnosed. It was part of my life and I couldn't imagine not talking about it. Cancer wasn't a dirty secret and I didn't want to hide it. The day I sent that tweet was one of the best days of my life. I was flooded with responses from people all over the world. I learned how to cope with chemotherapy from other patients. I met other doctors with cancer who understood what it was like being on the other side of the table. Through blogging I could reach out and help others, whilst getting help myself. The online cancer community is now a powerful force to be reckoned with – podcasts, campaigns, events are popping up everywhere and the real voice of cancer is being seen. This is really empowering, and gives people who are newly diagnosed hope – they are not alone, and there is live to be lived, even with a cancer diagnosis.

Emma

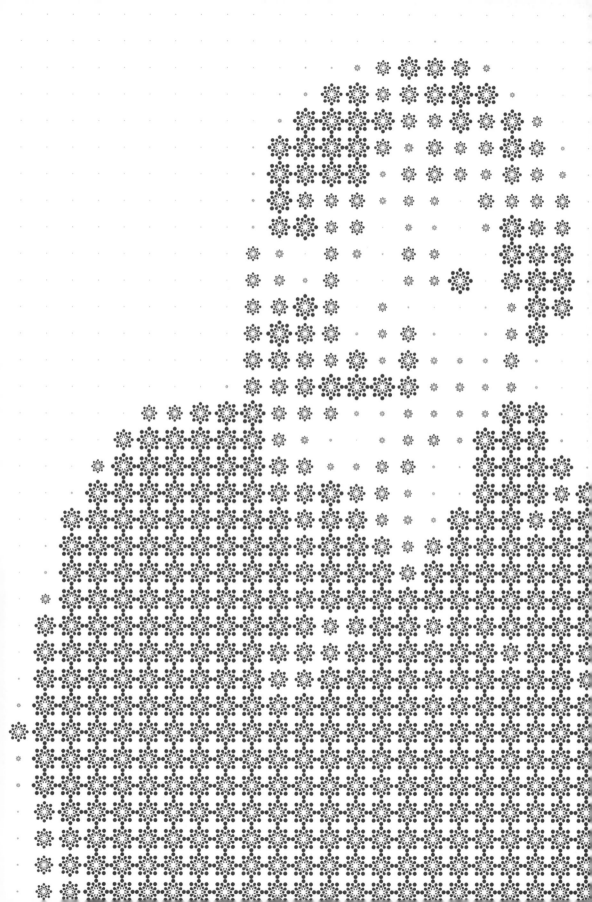

060

Cancer has changed so many different aspects of my life – some for better, some for worse. There are times when I feel that cancer has robbed me of my self-confidence, my fitness, my energy, my mental health, my financial stability and my understanding of my place within the world and where I fit within it moving forward. However, on a more positive note, I live my life far more in balance and more consciously than I did previously. I don't sweat the small stuff and I have a much clearer sense of perspective on what and who are important in my life now. I appreciate time with the people I love so much more than I did before, and in many ways, I am stronger now and more in tune with the true me. It has given me a sense of purpose in the form of the business that I have set up to help other people affected by cancer, and I have met and been inspired by so many truly amazing people – so maybe this is where the universe was leading me all along.

Early detection is so important. I never in a million years expected that I would hear the words, 'you have cancer' – that was something that happened to other people, older people, people who looked ill, not people like me. I was the fittest and healthiest I have ever been at the point when I was diagnosed (age 40). If people don't expect it to happen to them, if they don't realise that cancer doesn't necessarily look like the mental image they have in their head, then they won't have problems checked out or be too easily fobbed off, rather than demanding answers to abnormal symptoms. This reduces chances of early diagnosis. Open conversation about it will help people realise that yes, it could happen to them and yes, they should get that abnormal symptom checked out.

I think there is a vibrant and thriving social media cancer community that you will never know is there until you need it. However, once you uncover it, it is brilliant for helping you to feel less alone, and a wealth of experience, advice and support to help you through from people who 'get it'.

Danielle

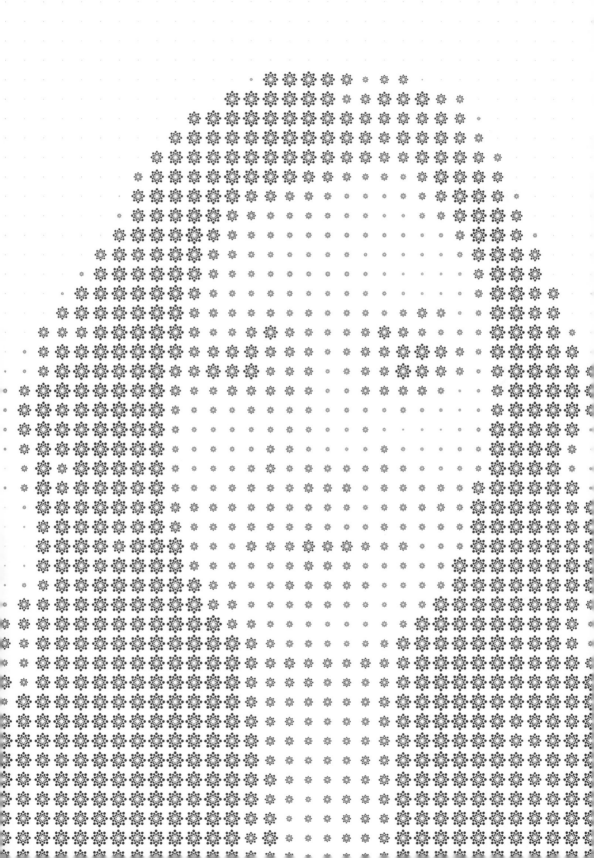

061

I was diagnosed in February 2018, after suffering symptoms for just under a year. My symptoms started during pregnancy, so myself and my doctor/midwife just assumed they were pregnancy related. When they didn't clear up after having my son I went back to the doctor on, I think, three occasions. I was given various laxatives and fibre supplements and told to keep a food diary for suspected Irritable Bowel Syndrome (IBS). Eventually I requested further investigation and was sent for a scope.

I never in a million years considered it could be cancer. This is why it's so important to spread awareness. Anytime I searched for my symptoms online, one of the main facts for bowel cancer was being over the age of 50. There was a very low chance that I could have bowel cancer at 31. Had I known this was a real possibility I might've pushed for investigation quicker. It may not have made any difference to my staging, but who knows? By the time I was diagnosed it had spread to my lymph nodes and liver. I was told inoperable and incurable.

No one likes talking about bathroom habits and many people would be embarrassed to discuss symptoms with their doctor. Whilst some will manage to do this once, how many will repeatedly go back and push for tests after being initially fobbed off with IBS? People could literally be dying of embarrassment and not want to be a pest. We need to educate both the general public and healthcare professionals that bowel cancer in young people is increasing and this is no longer an 'older' person's disease.

Cancer is undoubtedly the hardest thing that has happened to me and my family. On a positive note, it has given me great clarity on what is important in life and what I want to achieve in a potentially short period of time. I just hope I can kick the can down the road long enough for them to develop more promising treatments and give me as much time as possible with my family.

Emma-Louise

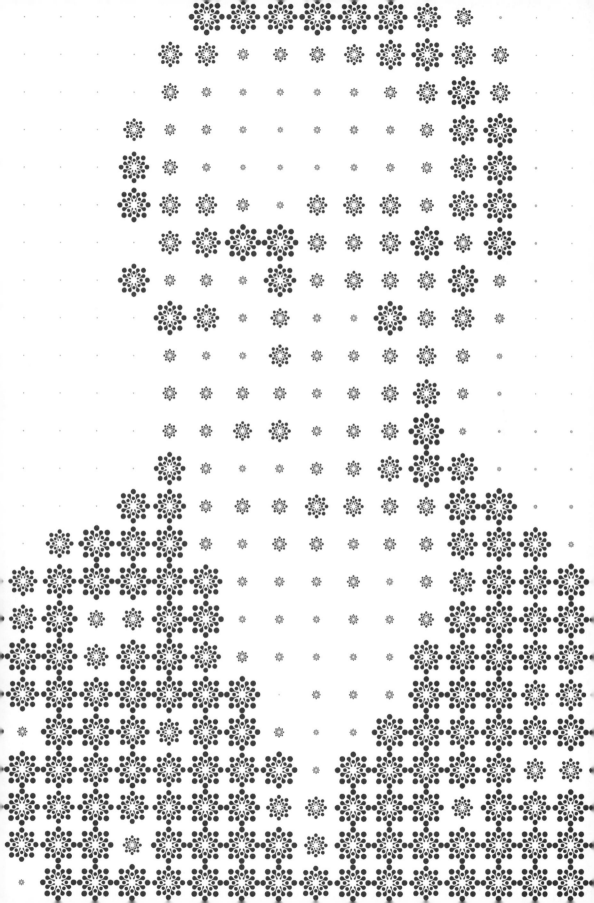

062

People never spoke about cancer in the past because they were terrified of it. You can't blame them; survival rates were so low that it's not surprising. Diagnosis' of cancer are on the rise but so are the numbers of people surviving the disease. Yet people still brush mentions of it under the carpet in the same way Harry Potter characters would refer to Voldemort – a 'thing' that must not be named. It makes no sense. Don't get it wrong, cancer is scary and comes with a lot of problems, but we aren't going to solve them by keeping our mouths shut and acting like they don't exist. When we refuse to talk about cancer, we keep people unaware of the signs and symptoms of the different types of the disease. It hinders your relationship with your body and health by disallowing you from taking responsibility for both of those things. Awareness means early detection and that can save lives. Keeping people in the dark can prove fatal, society lets them down.

It is important for me to talk about my trek with cancer. Showing the world that the disease doesn't discriminate based on age, especially for the stereotypical 'old people' cancers. We need to change the face of cancer by showing people that there is no 'face'. There are faces because no one is immune to cancer. That gets people talking and taking action. Speaking up means that those of us in minority cancer groups have our issues heard and met. This can trickle out from our corner of hospital life into the wider world and help people understand the reality of cancer and what support we need at different stages.

Cancer has greatly affected my life. Not only was I diagnosed with breast cancer, but three weeks earlier, my ma passed away from the same thing. One thing that has changed due to my own diagnosis is that I've found a community and my voice. I began writing and used Instagram as a blog to document my 'cancer milestones', discuss talking-points and find others who understood the cancer experience. Those are two things I never thought cancer would give me. They help me in my physical, mental and emotional recovery.

I've always believed that talking about our demons gives us power over them and a sense of freedom from them, even if it's only for a few hours. When enough of the fear melts away, that is when we make moves to improve life and start using that freedom to move forward.

Jenny

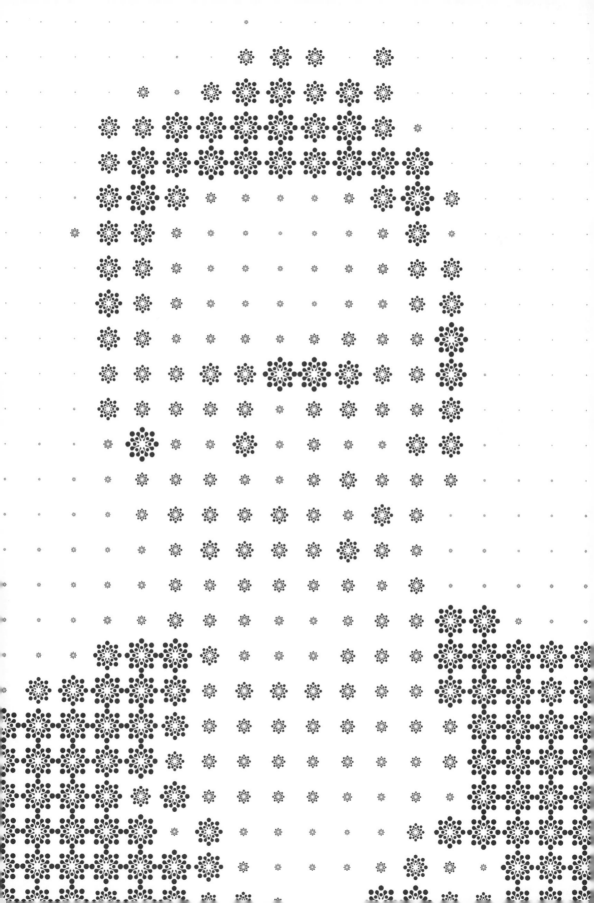

063

I had breast cancer when I was 45 years old, that was just over 10 years ago. It affected me in all sorts of ways. I am a doctor, a GP, so I thought I understood. I actually had no idea how individual everyone's cancer is, even when it is the same type. I had a mastectomy and really struggled. Not so much with the image, but with the fear of getting cancer in the other breast, as my sister also had breast cancer at the same time. Also, before cancer I enjoyed running, but running with one E-cup breast is not easy. It took me six years to persuade them to give me a second mastectomy (in which they found pre-cancerous cells, so I was vindicated). I then had a reconstruction and instead of nipples I have butterflies tattooed across them.

When I had my cancer, I was on Facebook but not on Twitter. I am a Christian and am active in the Church. I shared with online friends, church friends and colleagues and was very open about my diagnosis. It was also a great way to be supported in prayer. On the other hand, my sister told hardly anyone. She was very private about it and had a wig, whereas I wore scarves and made my chemotherapy obvious. My observation from this is that it was far harder to be an onlooker than to actually have the disease.

I joined Twitter three years ago when I was trying to fundraise for the London Marathon (for guide-dogs) and have really enjoyed it. It was through Twitter that I followed Liz O'Riordan and Trish Greenhalgh, as a fellow GP. I then got involved in Liz's medics with cancer WhatsApp group. As I am 10 years post diagnosis and now at the age of 56, an experienced GP, I have been able not only to gain support from the group through some tough situations, but also to support others. I have also learned lots more about certain medicines from different specialists. In addition, it has been great to talk to and meet some of the other group members in real life.

I am also a keen park-runner and have recently become an ambassador for 5K Your Way, along with having led my practice to become a park-run practice and most of the advertising for this has been virtual.

Claire

064

I nursed my mum through cancer, and so knew cancer as a carer first. I don't know which is harder. We recalibrate luck when we get cancer, so I can say I was lucky, compared to some – my cancer was caught in time, and treatable, but it has still turned my world upside down. I already loved life, but my experience of cancer has made me even more in love with life. I think I've become a bit more mindful, and a bit more compassionate. I cry a lot, over daft things, but I feel like that's ok. Sometimes – for example, when I'm trying to inch myself into a very cold lido – I remind myself what I've been through, and I feel that if I have managed that, I can cope with anything.

Support groups may seem the last thing you'd want, but in my experience they were fantastic to know I wasn't alone, as well as to laugh, and get great advice, and talk amongst others who would not be totally freaked out by fear of saying the wrong thing, or because of their own dread. If we remain invisible to each other, we can't realise how many of us have survived, and we can't devise strategies to cope.

I have made some extraordinary friends through Facebook, Twitter and Instagram – for example, women who (like me) have chosen not to have reconstructive surgery, post mastectomy, and who I would certainly not have met otherwise. Closed Facebook groups can be really helpful, especially when you don't have the energy during treatment to travel, or if you're isolated. They can be useful for sharing information, experiences and giving each other support.

My own work (as a writer and visual artist) is around women, health, identity, and visibility. I perform a life modelling monologue, 'Truth Is Beauty' and share the drawings on social media, which immediately increases the visibility of single-breasted women and opens up a dialogue. Nothing to hide, nothing to be ashamed of. It's making a difference, one drawing at a time.

Ellen

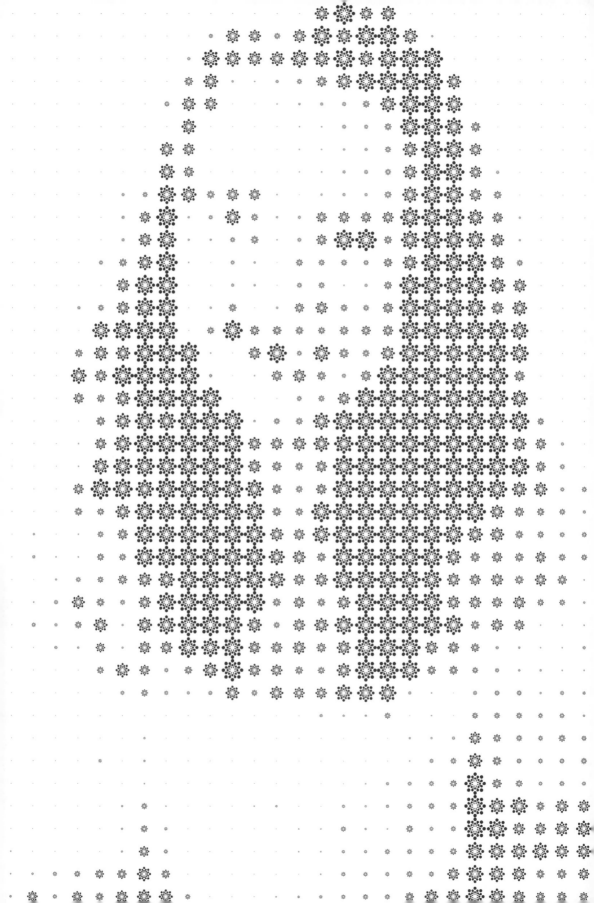

065

My whole life has changed because of cancer. Before cancer I was carefree and had no worries but that all changed the moment I was diagnosed – from that moment my main focus was survival. I had Acute Promyelocytic Leukaemia when I was nine and 12, and instantly my life changed. I went from my main focus being school and friendships to having no friends, being completely isolated and on horrendous treatment which was both lifesaving but also life changing. I had a stroke, caused by cancer and my doctors thought I'd never walk or talk again. Luckily, I'm doing just that, but I'm not where I was pre-cancer and it's taken me years to adjust to this new way of life. I'm now 23 years old and have since had nine brain surgeries for hydrocephalus, chronic migraine, chronic fatigue, viral encephalitis and postural orthostatic tachycardia syndrome. All because of cancer or the side effects of treatment. I know my life is different to what it was before and sometimes I think about what could have been. There are days where I get upset, but these are the cards I've been dealt, and I am just thankful for every well day that I have.

I believe that there needs to be understanding and conversation about cancer. Especially the late effects of cancer, although I look 'well' I am still living with the effects of cancer and my treatment daily. People don't understand this. To society I just look like any other young adult, but the amount of times I have been questioned about my health is crazy. This is why society needs to be informed so that others don't have the distress that I have had in the past.

I think social media has definitely opened up this discussion. For me, social media is a place for me to tell my story and for others to gain an insight into what it's like to be a young adult living post-cancer. Many of my friends write blogs and, once again, they show others what it's like to live with cancer in an honest and real way. Social media has also given me a place to write my feelings and thoughts on days that have been tough to not only inform others, but to help me too. Social media has also allowed me to connect with others going through cancer and I have made so many online friends who I can chat to and who just 'get it'. One in two of us will now get cancer, so it'll affect all of us in some way. So, I think the more discussion and openness, the better.

Jo

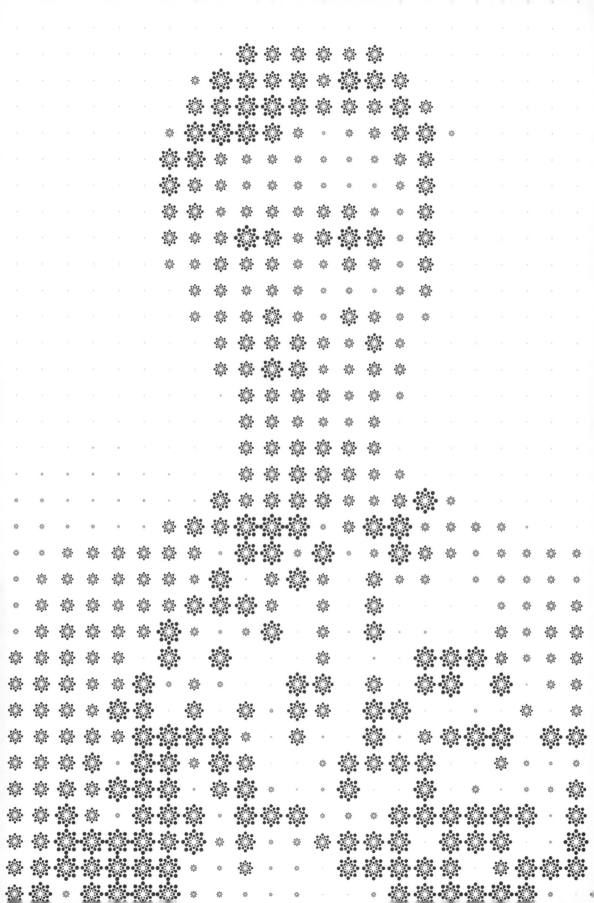

066

Cancer has affected me enormously. I was on maternity leave when I was diagnosed, my daughter was five months old and my son was nearly two and a half. So, everything changed. Surgery, treatment, radiotherapy and an early menopause at 38 years old. That was 12 years ago, but five years ago I was re-diagnosed with secondary breast cancer which had metastasised to my neck nodes and sternum bone. Now after five and a half years of five further cycles of chemotherapy, a neck re-section, removal and replacement of the sternum, radiotherapy and treatment every three weeks it has changed me completely. I've just finished treatment number 86. I have to have a treatment every three weeks to help stop the cancer returning, so you end up on maintenance treatment for life. I am incurable so there's no beating it – you have to live with it. Life is never the same when you've had cancer.

I don't think it should be 'normalised' as there is nothing normal about something invading you to try to kill you. I think it is pandemic proportions. Awareness of secondary cancer with red flag symptoms like my #sbcinfographic should be shared widely to help others spot the symptoms. People need to understand what secondary breast cancer is, the lack of clinical trials for patients, lack of surgeries and the issues with drug access that are supposed to help you keep alive and live a good quality of life for as long as possible – sadly it's not like that. People don't always get some or all of these things to help them live longer. That is why I started the #BusyLivingWithMets campaign to show that it wasn't immediate death. We are living with this disease but to live well we need those things mentioned to survive longer. I am lucky that I had a proactive oncologist who helped me get access to drugs on the Cancer Drugs Fund and referred me to non-standard surgeries. We should all have these options.

A huge part is social media, from the amazing community who are there 24/7 – you can use the hashtags #bccww or #bcsm and there is always going to be someone who answers you at 3am in the morning when you can't sleep. It builds amazing communities and support for all patients and clinicians need to be a part of the discussion so that they can learn from patient experience. It can help them with their own patients in their clinics. It's been a huge support for patients and carers alike. Our #bccww (breast cancer chat worldwide) community have a chat every Tuesday night at 9 to 10pm. It helps highlight many breast cancer issues. I created my website (ABC Diagnosis) for exactly this reason – to support patients. Signposting and blogging is an invaluable resource for patients, for sharing information.

Kevin

067

My journey started in December 2015. After suffering with stomach problems, I was sent for an endoscopy. In January 2016, I had a phone call from the consultant, he said 'I would like to refer you to see a Haematologist, are you okay with this?'. To which I said, 'Ok'. This was on a Friday and my appointment was for the following Tuesday. I did not think anything of this, I just wanted the pain to go away. On the Tuesday I turned up at East Surrey Hospital and booked in. I was asked to have a blood test and then await my appointment. When I was ushered into my appointment, I was met with a Haematologist and a Macmillan Nurse, who asked me if I had brought someone with me. Having no letter of the appointment, I did not know I needed anyone. I was then told I had Non-Hodgkin's Lymphoma and would need some more tests to diagnose what type and how far it had spread. The problem Lymph Node was sat just above my Duodenum (the first part of the small intestine). Following a PET/CT scan and Bone Marrow biopsy I was told I had low grade Lymphoma and would be put on 'Watch and Wait'. This included monthly appointments for further reviews.

Watch and Wait lasted two months, with my symptoms getting worse. So, in April 2016 I started my first chemotherapy treatment (Rituximab/Bendamustine). This was given over two days and repeated every four weeks, for six cycles. I was lucky in that I only had one really bad session, the first one, where I was ill over the weekend following the treatment. After the six cycles I had another PET/CT scan and was told I was in remission. I was also told that even though I was in remission for cancer, I would never get rid of Non-Hodgkin's Lymphoma, but the aim was to keep me in remission for as long as possible.

The next stage was to put me onto maintenance treatments, these consisted of Rituximab injections every two months with follow up appointments and lasted for 12 sessions. After six cycles and me developing a number of side effects – a bad chesty cough, peripheral neuropathy and Type 2 Diabetes – it was decided that it would be best to stop the treatment. I still attend regular appointments and am still in remission. I also have managed to get myself into a pre-diabetic state by making major lifestyle changes.

Even though I will never be rid of my Non-Hodgkin's Lymphoma, I class myself as one of the lucky ones. I have managed to get on top of this with the great help of my family friends and my Cancer support Centre The Olive Tree Crawley. The best way I found to help me get to this state of mind is by talking about my journey and being positive about it.

Dave

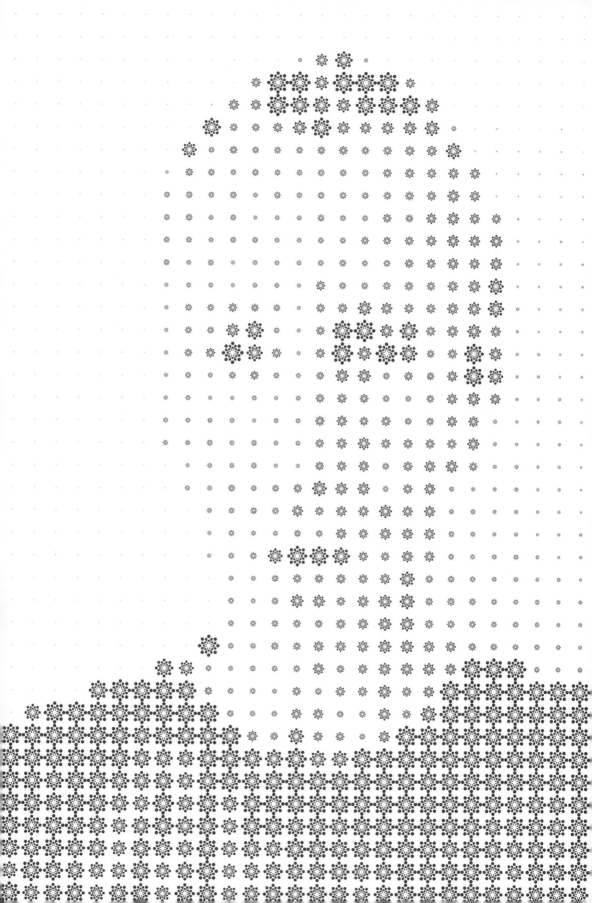

068

In 2004 my wife was diagnosed with breast cancer. Luckily, it was in situ in a duct and was successfully removed. A course of radiation followed and after five years she was given the all clear.

Unfortunately, after a long period of having pains in her sit bones she was diagnosed with a different type of breast cancer in the other breast. It wasn't the original cancer returning. A mastectomy was recommended but further tests revealed it had spread to the bones, every organ and brain. Devastating news. Amazingly, she responded well to chemotherapy, despite being hospitalised several times. She lived well for five more years, had around 70 rounds of chemotherapy and four lots of gamma knife to brain lesions. Things got much worse last year as tumours were growing in her spinal cord which disabled her. Eventually she became totally bed ridden and so weak and confused. Death was a welcome release from her suffering.

For good measure, in late 2013, I discovered a lump in my jawline which turned out to be Squamous Cell Carcinoma. I was treated with chemotherapy and radiotherapy – seven rounds of Cetuximab (a type of chemotherapy) and 35 sessions of radiotherapy. It was so brutal, my face was burnt to hell and looked like pizza toppings. I was unable to eat solids for months and lost 20kg. But eventually most of it healed and I am four and a half years post treatment and doing well. My mouth constantly burns, and eating is difficult. But I kept all my teeth, produce saliva and my speech isn't really affected. So, I was lucky.

During this treatment I was also treated for Hepatitis C, with a new drug which cleared the virus. Having had Hepatitis C, one was given regular liver CT scans because the risk of liver cancer increases. A year ago, a tumour was found in my liver. This has been treated twice using Chemoembolisation (TACE) and I am waiting to see if the last treatment was successful. This will only buy some time, it isn't curative. So, sometime in the next few years I expect my liver to start failing. But I have been expecting an early demise for a long time and am at peace with that. I have no dependents apart from my dog and there's plenty of people who will look after her.

I do think people need to talk more about cancer and dying. Cancer is scary, but ignoring it doesn't make it go away. I think there is so much one doesn't know unless they have seen someone go through treatment.

As for death, cancer kills many people. We need to accept that and face it, make the most of each day while it's possible. I'm getting on just fine, for now, and hope to stay this way but I know it will change eventually and then I'll have to plan my exit.

Andrew

069

Diagnosed with Prostate Cancer three years ago. Chance discovery when a full blood test, taken before a varicose vein operation, revealed a PSA (a blood test to help detect prostate cancer) of 93. No real symptoms before diagnosis.

A prostate biopsy showed cancerous cells to be occupying most of the prostate, with some breakthroughs into the lymph node areas. A prostatectomy was the initial course of action as the cancer was still considered to be mostly localised. Tests after the surgery revealed a lingering trace of PSA in the blood, which suggested there were still cancerous cells present. An eight-week follow-up adjuvant course of radiation therapy was undertaken with a resulting undetectable reading of PSA – a good result that has now been maintained for the last two years.

So far, I consider myself to be one of the lucky ones. I do have some side effects from the procedures I underwent, but, in general, I am quite healthy and lead a normal life. My physical appearance is unchanged apart from a few scars left from the surgery required to remove the Prostate. Ongoing PSA tests are required to ensure it remains undetectable. These have now moved to 12-monthly intervals, where initially they were every six months.

Cancer comes in many forms, some more dangerous to life than others, but all cancers carry a stigma to some degree. In times past, when cures were in their infancy, being diagnosed with cancer often meant a sufferer would likely die as a result of the disease. This of course meant that the disease would be discussed in hushed tones and often not discussed at all. This would have left the patient in a very isolated place, a place no one would have wanted to be while suffering a terminal illness.

Thankfully things are slowly improving, in both cures and the openness of discussion about one's illness. There are still the terms bandied around like 'You have to fight this', 'You must stay positive', 'Winning the Battle', 'Losing the Battle', and so on. These are all well-meant but don't really help the sufferer of the disease. All cancer sufferers know this only too well that this kind of language seems to separate those with the condition from others, and in some way reinforces the cancer stigma. Regardless of the condition one is suffering from, there are many life-threatening ailments. Cancer is just another one of these, and these days survival rates are constantly improving for most cancer types, with breakthroughs in immunotherapy and ongoing studies into all aspects of the disease. It's slow, it's complicated, but it's happening.

So, the more we get cancer out into the open, treat it as just another disease (albeit an often serious one) and talk about it in normal terms, the easier people will feel about the whole cancer thing. This will greatly benefit sufferers and supporters alike. It's just another of life's illnesses, along with all the others that threaten the human race. No more, no less.

Alan

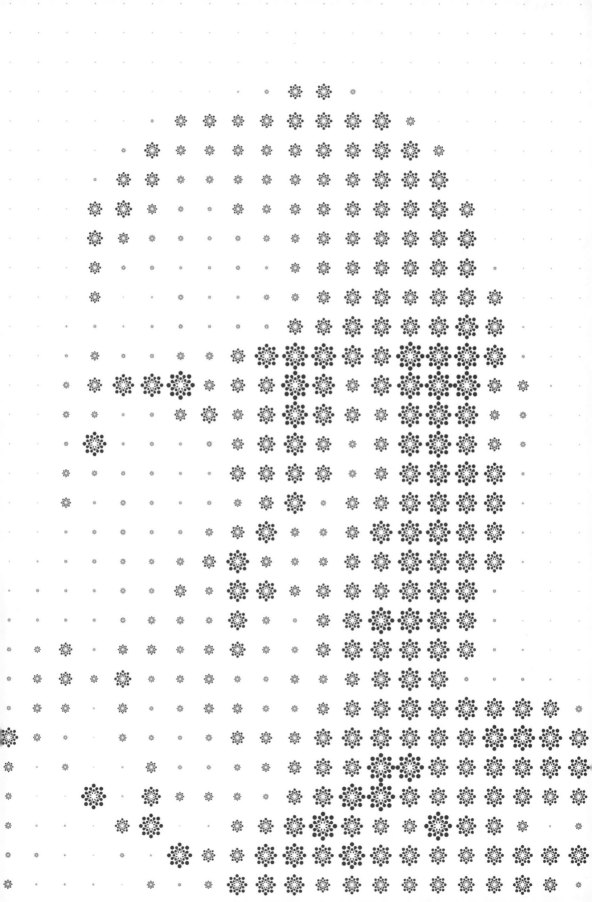

070

Before my diagnosis at age 65 I had, over the years, become a little self-centred, perhaps selfish and absorbed in myself. This, despite being married for 43 years and with three grown up children, with families of their own. After the shock of being told I had aggressive prostate cancer had passed, I felt extremely sorry for myself and became mildly depressed after I was told I could have five to ten years left. I then snapped out of it and looked back at my life and realised how lucky I had been with wife children, grandchildren and family. My wife attended every one of my radiotherapy sessions, Monday to Friday, she drove when I was fatigued by the treatment. She has supported me through mood swings and marital issues caused by hormone therapy without a word of complaint. We are now very much closer than before my cancer and I realise I had been taking her for granted for a long time. It's strange that I have cancer to thank for making me a much different and better person since diagnosis. I appreciate and value what I have and am determined to make the most of what time I have left, however long that may be. I have become a volunteer at my local hospital on the Patients Council and I am active on sub-committees, because I am determined to give something back for the excellent care I have received from the NHS.

It was only for a short while I kept my diagnosis to myself, but one night the topic came up in conversation at my local pub, when a friend was talking about his wife having breast cancer. I opened up in front of three or four friends and was amazed at the support I got, in fact two of my friends had close family members with prostate cancer. My family all know and in fact my youngest daughter visited last weekend, just after I had my first very short haircut ready for the summer. She said to my wife and me, 'Well Dad, at least it looks like you've got cancer now'. We were laughing for quite a while and that sums up my attitude now – to how I am dealing with my cancer.

For the last year I have been a prolific member on the Prostate Cancer UK website. When I was diagnosed, I went there in desperation to get information from fellow cancer sufferers. They helped me immensely by dispelling rumours/false information and giving me informed help on where my 'journey' would take me. Now I am on the site regularly and find myself helping people who are in the same situation now, as I was a year ago.

Last year I decided to enter a cycle event from Bristol to Weston Super Mare that was advertised on Facebook. Then I saw an appeal on the Prostate Cancer UK Website to fundraise for them. I setup a JustGiving page and used Facebook to ask all of my 300 plus friends to pledge money. In the end I raised £1,200. All of my Facebook friends have been so very supportive, and I find this so helpful. I am new to Twitter, but without it I would not be writing this now to you. I have a growing following and am slowly selecting groups, a lot of which are cancer related.

Sally

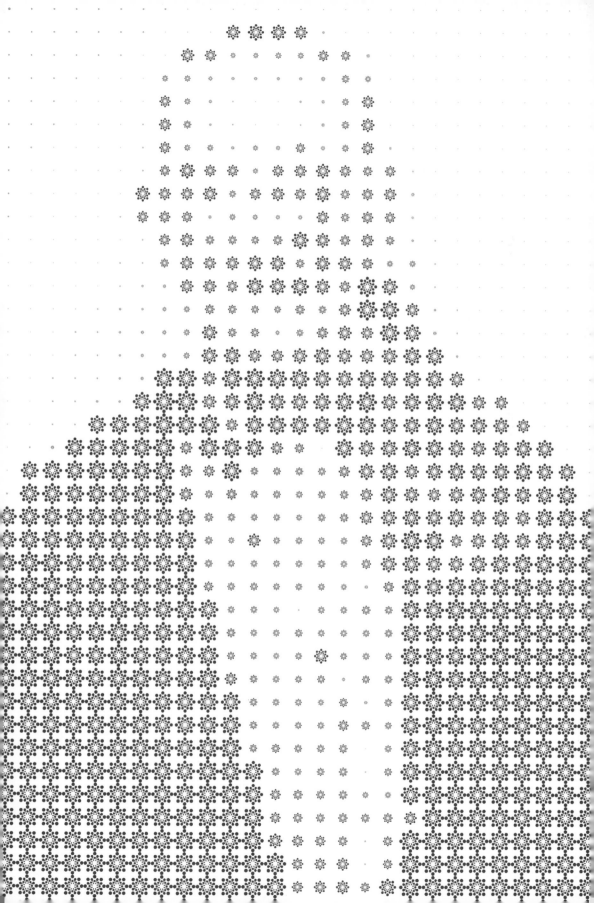

071

A little bit about me and the cancer: first mammogram on the 5th of April 2018; follow up mammogram and five biopsies taken on the 12th of April 2018; diagnosed with right side multifocal pT1c (11 x 6 x 4mm) Grade 3 (T3P3M3) invasive ductal Carcinoma with extensive high-grade comedo DCIS (over 110mm) on the 19th of April 2019 (no LVI, pN1 (one macrometastasis in one lymph node, which was removed); ER7, PgR 0, HER2 3+ on primary; ER 8, PgR 0, HER2 3+ on involved lymph node); began Herceptin injections every three weeks on the 26th September 2019; began weekly paclitaxel chemotherapy every week for 12 weeks with a cold cap on the 13th December 2018; a Zoledronic acid (Zometa) drip on the 13th December 2018 and began Letrazole 2.5mg tablets on the 28th December 2018.

Before the breast cancer, I had cervical cancer at age 23 (in 1987) and had radical hysterectomy and no further treatment. My mother passed in 1977 of cervical cancer at the age of 41, so didn't have her to fall back on. I found it weird, back then, as everyone else on the ward and in the clinic was twice my age. I had little point of reference to refer to back then. I just got on with it, as if it was the same as having my tonsils out. I never wanted children so that wasn't an issue and I just got on with life.

I was then diagnosed with the Ductal carcinoma in situ (DCIS, a non-invasive breast cancer) last year and that was a bit of a shock. But, I had a similar attitude to the previous time and thought, 'It is what it is'. To be honest, the shock of needing the chemotherapy and the threat of losing, my then waist length hair and lovely long eyelashes was more traumatic. But I muscled through with the chemotherapy and Paxman cold cap and still have my hair (as you can see by my portrait).

I have always openly spoken about my cancer experiences. I do not fear death. We all have that ahead of us, inevitably. So, I find myself having a realistic approach to it. It's happened now, what can be done? There are so many emotions to process at the time, but they seem to fall to one side in the chaos of appointments tests and clinics. It's only later you get to process them. In the days of your recovery, I feel more needs to be done to prepare you for that part of the process. I don't like using the phrase 'my journey'. A journey is something you take out of choice with a destination at the end. No one would choose a journey to cancer.

I hate that cancer is still shrouded in taboo, even in 2019, and is still a subject spoken about in whispers and hushed voices. I think it's important to be open and vocal – we need to kill off the stigma and fear associated with cancer. I do have my dark days and low moods, the same as anyone, but on the whole feel positive about the future.

I am under The Royal Marsden Hospital at Sutton and they have been amazing from the get-go. My experience this past year has been a lot better than it could have been. The staff have been brilliant and very early on I decided I would love to work there to be part of this amazing organisation and give a little something back in some way. I am literally in the middle of a job application for a role there, so fingers crossed.

Allie

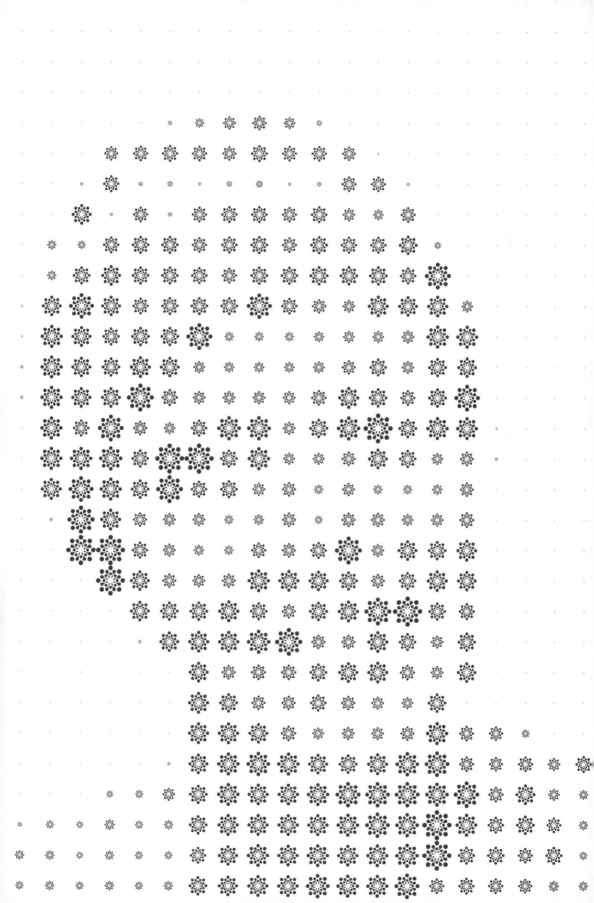

072

At 42, while living in Senegal, I found a small pea-sized lump in my breast and had a mammogram within 24 hours. I had no history of breast cancer in my family, I breast fed my two children (now four and seven years old) and really had no risks for cancer. The radiologist said he didn't see anything unusual in my mammogram and that I should return in six months to see if the lump had changed. I had a gut feeling that something was wrong. Instead of waiting, I started researching. I learned that I had dense breasts and that a standard mammogram wasn't enough. I went with my gut and made an appointment with a specialist in Boston who turns around results in 24 hours. Sure enough, stage 3, Invasive ductal carcinoma (IDC) – additionally I found out I am BRCA2+.

Cancer uprooted my life – my children and husband packed up and came to the USA to help me navigate the medical system and support me. A five-day business trip turned into 10 months of gruelling treatment and two surgeries (there is still another one in the future). Before I had breast cancer, I thought that it was easy to treat, and people could move on with their lives after treatment... I was wrong.

Not only do I have side effects from chemotherapy, surgery and radiation, I have to face ten years of pill popping to keep cancer away. I struggle with the treatment plan every day. Monthly injections to suppress my ovaries and daily exercises to keep lymphedema away. I feel that my femininity is slipping away with each pill I swallow, to block my oestrogen (this is daily). I wake at night grasping for my wedding ring and sigh in relief when it twirls on my finger as it means I made it another day without lymphedema. My hair is growing back, but I have lost parts of my sexuality – as a young married woman this is a hard fact to face.

We need a global effort to Save the Women – as we are dying. We know the numbers in developed countries, but in developing countries, many women die undiagnosed or cannot be treated due to the lack of services or accessibility to services. Open and transparent dialogs with healthcare professionals, as well as the general population are critical to our survival.

My top six are:

1. Breast Cancer diagnosis and treatment is inequitable globally, geographic location, age, gender, socio-economic status, ethnicity and race play a major role in survival – we need further research to understand this and funds to act on the recommendations from research.

2. Dense Breasts equates to the need of a 3D mammogram.

3. Breast Cancer treatment is a lifelong commitment and isn't easy – we need to advocate for more research to stop the epidemic (yes, I am calling it an epidemic).

4. Prognosis of living after Breast Cancer treatment is inequitable. There needs to be standards for care for all with a goal of rolling out globally.

5. 'Wait and See' should never be an option and results from biopsies need to be fast tracked.

6. Oestrogen blocking after a breast cancer diagnosis needs to be transparent and at front and centre for young women.

If we don't block it, we may have a re-occurrence. If we do block it, our quality of life changes. We need support on how to manage as young pre-menopausal women who have been forced into menopause as part of treatment.

Greer

073

Strong, fit, healthy, happy 42-year-old, a mother, a wife, a daughter, a friend. Breast cancer seemingly stripped this away, brutally, unashamedly exploding into every part of my life and the people I loved. Shock, scared, sadness, anger, guilt, weak, pain, sick – suddenly this was me. I felt let down by my body and in turn I had let everyone else down. Arguing with myself I wasn't ill, just a lump, I was fit and healthy – constant chatter in my mind. How? Why me? Why not me?

I am still very early in my cancer experience, six months in. I already know I will be changed, I feel very different, I will forever look different, but I am also incredibly lucky. I have such wonderful family and amazing friends and cancer only served to feed their love and strength. My body is working hard for me, and for them, and I am starting to trust in it again, baby steps but steps all the same.

The first few days of just my husband and I knowing I had cancer were truly horrendous. It however was the burden of not talking, compared to the act of sharing, discussing, communicating, that had a truly dramatic impact. Being able to talk about our rapidly developing new normal felt like such a relief. The diagnosis hadn't changed, the conversation however had commenced. Open conversation once started doesn't go quiet and, as the stats illustrate, neither will cancer. Cancer is, and will continue to be for many of us, simply part of life. The cancer conversation is therefore intrinsic in helping us all to live our best life. My conversation I feel has removed some of the fear, the guilt, the myths, the isolation, the ignorance. Cancer isn't going anywhere and, if it ever beckons again for me, a loved one, their loved ones and so on, we are already talking, and this is a gift.

Erratically scrambling around the internet looking for comfort, for cures, for answers, for positive stories and on occasions for the negatives. Downloading books, browsing forums, reading blogs, listening to podcasts, especially between 2am and 5am in the darkness, alone. This has its place, I needed to do this, to empower and inform me upon my initial diagnosis. I also realised I was more absorbing, not talking, not interacting and this was not going to be effective in the long term. I proceeded to nudge into social media, something I hadn't explored in any personal aspect of my life before (pure business participation in the past). I remember my first cancer post, nothing major, just a question but, like that, the conversation had started. I was suddenly active, not passive, I could talk to people with cancer, impacted by cancer, had a relationship with cancer. I could seek suggestions and I could offer suggestions. The cancer world suddenly grew, I was part of this group that none of us ever wanted to be in, but you were bloody glad when you found it. My conversation grew. My family, friends, and social media all had a role in the cancer conversation and in turn we all benefited directly and indirectly from each other. Learning, sharing, questioning, helping each other, even if each other didn't know they had! The world can feel very scary, but technology is a communication enabler and really can play a fundamental role in helping us all navigate and communicate life with all its ups and downs.

Angela

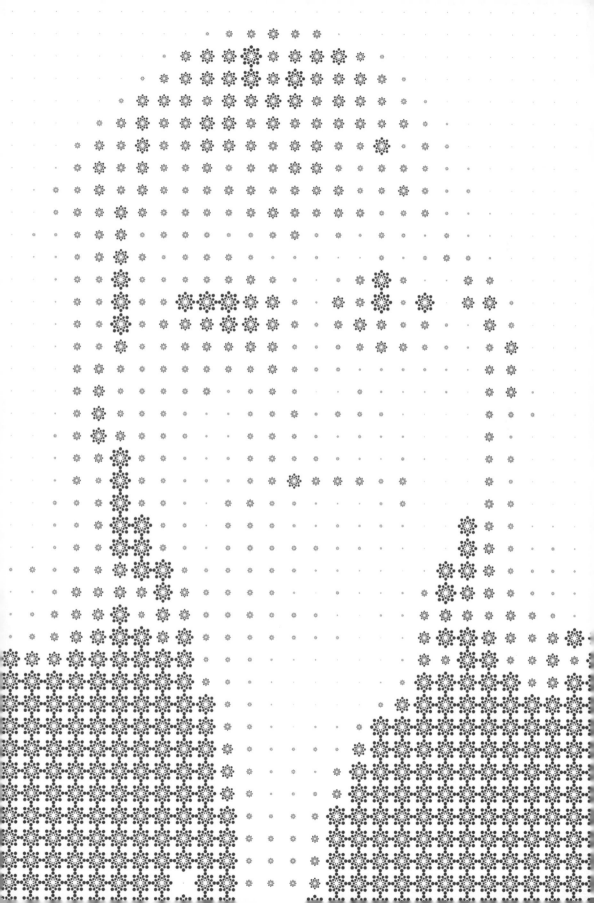

074

I've seen my Father, Mother-in-law and Husband go through treatment for the disease. My husband continues to live with two inoperable brain tumours and my Mother-in-law was recently diagnosed with breast cancer (her second cancer). Each of them took the approach of head down and just get on with treatment. No point in complaining or discussing it. All three of them were, and are, stoic and did not/do not talk about their illness, fears or the hideous side effects of their treatment. They don't want anyone to know that they are ill and fighting cancer. They never tell people about their cancer.

I think they believe if they keep their feelings and illness to themselves, they are protecting us – their family. It's an immensely brave way to face a life-threatening illness but makes it incredibly difficult for those around them to know how to really help and behave, at times. They feel that by creating this bubble it allows the other members of the family, on the surface at least, to get on with a normal life. But the reality is many things go unspoken and everyone struggles with the consequences of living with cancer. For instance, you don't know when they are feeling really ill and may lose patience with them, when in fact this is the time to be patient. My husband was diagnosed when he was 35 years old and we are now 19 years further down the road. He has dealt with numerous forms and rounds of treatment.

Although he doesn't want people outside of the family to know, he supported me in telling our children at every stage what was going on. I read early on in a cancer information leaflet, don't scare your children with long explanations about the illness in its totality, but just deal/explain what is going on in the here and now, honestly and in terms they can understand.

So, when they were very young children: 'Why is Daddy not driving?' 'Daddy has two lumps in his head which cause epilepsy so he can't drive'; 'Why is Daddy going to hospital?' 'He had brain surgery, the lumps in his head have grown a bit too big, so the doctors need to make them smaller'; 'What pills are those?' 'Daddy's lumps have got too big again and so he is now taking pills to shrink them'. Then as they got older: 'My friends mother died of cancer, does Daddy have cancer?' 'Yes, it is a form of cancer. There are many types both high and low grade. We are very lucky and his are only a grade 2 slow growing, low grade type'; 'Are his lumps called tumours?' 'Yes, they are, it means a mass. We called them lumps when you were small so you could visualise what we meant'.

Taking part in open discussion on the Internet can be extremely helpful to people who themselves are open about their illness and experiences. Others, like my family members who are not open to discussion, may still find reading or watching what others say very helpful – reading it from the side-lines but not entering into the conversation.

Maybe I should have reached out on social media, because I found that nobody outside the home realises what is going on. So, you often feel burdened. When in public you have to work hard to cover for the person who is feeling ill, because they don't want people to know about their illness. You cannot force someone to be open about their illness and feelings. They choose how to deal with it. So, I salute three very brave people who carried/carry this burden alone.

Laura

075

For my sister Jean, it all started with a rare blood disease that was undiagnosed for quite a while. Jean was a 'Can Do' person and no task was ever too hard. At one time, Jean thought nothing of dragging a hundred-pound cement pig trough across her property in order to turn it into an outdoor planter. By the time Jean realised she had a health problem, she didn't have the strength to walk up a flight of stairs and could not hold a blow dryer over her head. The change in Jean's strength was dramatic.

Jean was finally diagnosed by doctors at Cleveland Clinic with 'Coldagluten', which meant that her red blood cells died from exposure to cold. She lived in Cleveland, Ohio located on the shores of Lake Erie (one of the Great Lakes) and it is not unusual for snow to be on the ground from early November until April. Darn cold. One would hope that the summers were better, but air conditioning had the same effect on her body. Jean was extremely anaemic with haemoglobin levels so critical that her heart could stop beating. Blood transfusions were started but they stopped being effective. Unfortunately, Jean's treatments were trial and error with problems along the way.

Jean went on for almost six years with whatever treatments her doctors suggested, only treating the symptoms but never curing the problem. As part of her treatment, Jean went in for a PET Scan in August 2014 that revealed she had masses in her body. The diagnosis of Lymphoma was added to her compromised system. Jean continued her frequent trips to the hospital but now the trips were for chemotherapy with a new team of doctors. When her beautiful chestnut hair fell out, she bought a wig. Jean threw up for the eight rounds of chemotherapy until she was hospitalised for replacement fluids. The treatment for Jean seemed lethal. A bone marrow transplant was discussed but the blood needed to be cold for this process and that interfered with her Coldagluten that was still present. The chemotherapy treatments ended in the Spring 2015. For a brief moment, the doctors announced to Jean and Steve, her husband, 'Jean is in remission!' Jean told me they looked at each other, without cheering, and left the doctor's office. She did not believe them.

I saw Jean one month later, in May 2015. She was still very tired and taking medication. I asked her why she was taking medication and she said, 'Leukemia'. By August, Lymphoma was back. Jean swore she would never go through treatment again, not ever, but she did with worse results. Jean struggled until January, unable to sit up on her own, or eat or walk.

My beautiful, smart, generous, thoughtful, strong, intelligent, funny, darling sister Jean lost her battle with cancer on February 17, 2016. She was compromised for the last eight years of her life. Even knowing how much she suffered I miss her every single day. Jean was 68 years old, eldest of five sisters, a year older than myself, daughter to Anna (91 years old), wife to Steve for 48 years, mother of two sons, two daughters-in-law, grandmother of five, mentor to many, and my best friend.

In today's society, everybody wants to be politically correct (PC). In an effort to achieve PC, people avoid difficult topics such as religion, politics, and cancer. We often ask individuals when we meet, 'How are you?' but we are often hoping that the person will just answer, 'Fine!' – any other answer causes discomfort for both individuals. If a freedom existed in conversation, it could normalize the process, and lead to testing, diagnosis, treatment, and better rates of survival. Cancer is treatable; you just have to treat it.

Melanie

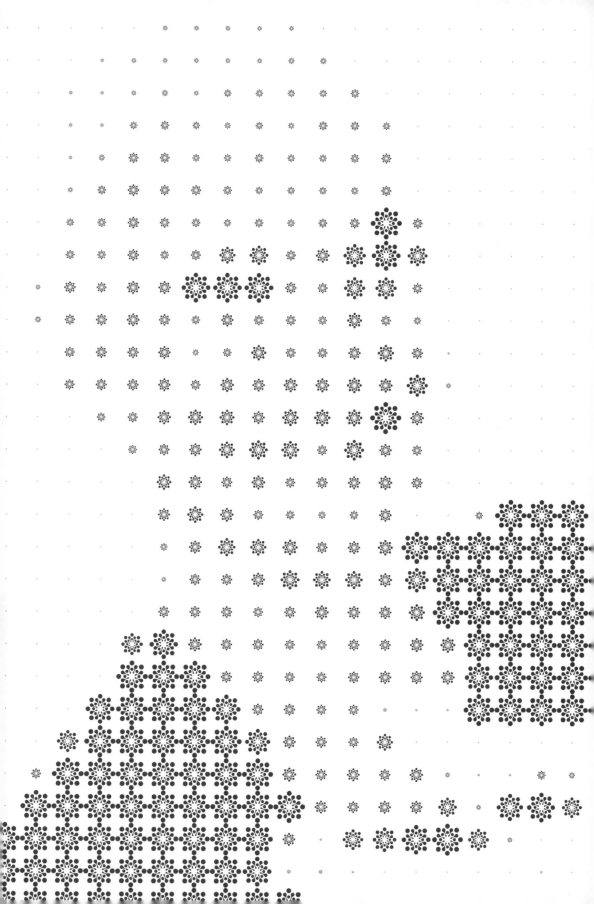

076

Cancer changed my life, my body, my perspective. I have changed so much; I hardly recognise myself as the same person that as I was before.

My brain function is slower. Though I have always been a highly functioning person who creates opportunity and thinks outside the box, this changed function, slower recall of words, affects me deeply. My body is changed. I no longer have breasts. I decided not to replace my loss and not to reconstruct or wear the form of breasts within my clothing. This has strengthened my persona, given me a sense of autonomy that I would never have imaged possible. It has unleashed a new sense of gender and a celebration of its expression for me. I have changed my diet. I no longer accept interpersonal treatment that does not sit well with me. I have become an outspoken advocate for women's bodily choice. I use my voice to challenge the medical community, who sometimes carry unchecked bias, and can unduly influence women to reconstruct to breast mound, with suggestions of feeling whole and looking good to others.

I participated in the Great Big Story film 'It's My Breasts or Nothing'. The last sentence, of which, says it all, for me. I want to talk about the flat reconstructive choice in order to empower women to trust in themselves and their own needs. I would like for women to understand that being breast-less also means being beautiful.

I am participating in the creation of a Non-Profit called Flat Closure NOW, so that patients can see images of women who reflect their desired aesthetic outcome, access supportive information related to their individual needs and find assurance that this is a valid, empowered and beautiful choice. We also want to connect surgeons to educational resources, amend the language in the WHCRA (Women's Health and Cancer Rights Act) to include 'flat closure' as a reconstructive type, and to help doctors code their insurance claims to support this outcome.

When I was first diagnosed, there were hardly any images of flat or single-breasted women, we were not gathering or acknowledging our choice. Historical precedent had set up a silence that I found to be constrictive and untrue to my personal needs, given the amount of changes this disease had brought into my life. After trying to prompt public figures like Kathy Bates and Tig Notaro (who also both chose flat), and receiving no response, I decided to be the change I wanted to see in the world. I have participated in high fashion photoshoots, posed for magazine articles and stood for interview in CBS Sunday Mornings, Beyond Cancer special. All because I felt the need to create space and allow this reconstructive choice to come to light.

Having been a craft book author and textile designer, I have a small following of mostly female artists in my social media feeds. I used this platform to bring my needs to their attention. My first act of participation was for a project called Grace, by Charise Isis. To release this image, I wrote an article on my artists blog, speaking to the challenges I experienced in going flat, within the medical community. Surprisingly this was really well received. From there, I was asked to participate in a photoshoot that would provide editorial content for a genderless underwear company. This went viral. Since this time, I have been able to hone my message and have caught the ear of the media and women around the world. I now host a Facebook group called My Flat Friends, whose members span the world. We support one another, no matter if we are flat, reconstructed to breast mound, seeking to explant or any other combination a breast cancer patient might experience. Never would I have thought any of this was possible, nor that I would have the confidence to share nude images of my person, on the internet. But I did.

Yvonne

077

At the time I was diagnosed with breast cancer in 2012 I was working as a Social Work practitioner with young offenders. I chose to tell my managers and my own team, of the diagnosis and of the surgery, as my colleagues had always been very supportive of me. I had hoped to be back at work quickly but hadn't bargained for the impact that the treatment would have on my other health issues. I was off work for a year but chose to keep in touch with work by dropping in every month or so, usually when I was on my way to King's College Hospital (KCH) in London for the next chemotherapy or appointment.

In September 2013 I was back at work but still felt off kilter. Colleagues were very supportive towards me and by the end of November I was beginning to feel more like my old self. In December I had some vaginal bleeding which I mentioned at my check-up. The hospital decided to have a look at things and ordered more tests. Professionally, my employers were going through a restructuring and we had to apply for jobs. I had an interview for a promotion on my last day at work before Christmas. The first week in January 2014 I had some biopsies taken, the surgeon came to see me and told me that what he had seen was too complex and that I would need CT Scans and an MRI.

Ten days later I was told that I had Uterine Carcinosarcoma – quite scary as KCH decided that it was too complex for them to deal with and they would need to find a specialist. Within a week I was at St Thomas' talking to a consultant who offered to keep me in that night and do the operation the next morning. Cue total panic and I asked if I could have a few days to get organised. Four days later I was admitted and had the surgery. It was whilst I was recovering from, what my family refer to as 'The Full Fillet', that I found out I had got the job I'd applied for.

Surgery was followed by more chemotherapy, radiotherapy and brachytherapy (internal radiation therapy) – so another year off of work. My employers kept the job for me, both they and my colleagues kept in touch with me, some even coming to keep me company on chemotherapy days. They kept that post open for me until I returned 13 months later, and I had a six-week phased return to work. The second cancer took a lot out of me, I found the chemotherapy drugs hard; I had a pulmonary embolism, as well, which was spotted through a CT scan. I'll never forget heading home after the scan and my consultant calling me to ask where I was. He then asked how far I was from a hospital's Accident and Emergency and told me to get there as soon as possible. I arrived at the other hospital to find a nurse waiting for me at the door. I was taken straight to a cubicle and then everything became blurred as they hooked me up to drips and gave me an injection. For the next few months my life revolved around hospitals, ongoing treatment and getting over my fear of needles by having to give myself daily injections.

My family live over 200 miles away and have a lot going on. My husband bore the brunt of the mood swings, physical illness and domestic stuff. I got a lot of support from my knitting group – another member was going through breast cancer at the same time as me, we swapped notes as our treatments were very different. I began posting about my cancers on my Facebook pages, as the easiest way to keep family and friends informed. I got a lot of support from doing this and soon began to realise that cancer treatments were still a closed book to many people. I gradually found online support groups and became more knowledgeable and then shared that knowledge with others. As a knitter I use Ravelry (a community site, an organizational tool, and a yarn & pattern database for knitters and crocheters) to keep in touch with friends around the world – I got a message from someone I didn't know, to say that she had just been diagnosed with Uterine Carcinosarcoma and could she ask me some questions. I answered as honestly as I could and we have kept in touch over the last four years, celebrating each other's clear check-ups etc.

The cancers have had a big impact on my life and on my family and friends. Some friends fell by the wayside, others have become much closer. I am a different person because of it. The challenge is to use what I have experienced/felt to help educate others.

Jan

078

Having a ridiculously positive personality did not prepare me for the dreadful diagnosis of breast cancer. Deep down I feared the worst but convinced myself that my inverted nipple was due to a minor problem with my milk ducts. The power of positive thinking would resolve everything – if only it was so simple. I consider myself to be an intelligent woman who would not miss the signs of something sinister. I went directly to my doctor and was referred within days. I recalled that a few months previously I had noticed a dry creamy blob on my nipple. As this did not reoccur, I thought no more of it. Around the same time my daughter Sophie asked how often I checked my breasts. Honestly, not as often as I should. I did so and thought that I felt one, two, three small lumps. Panic set in momentarily but then I could not find them again. Neither could my husband. As there were several of them and they had disappeared I assumed that they were of no consequence. A few months later I noticed the change to my nipple. I still could not feel any lumps, nor could my doctor. Within days of seeing him I had an appointment for a mammogram and ultrasound at my local Breast Clinic. There the nightmare began. I was totally unprepared for the immediate diagnosis, not expecting a verdict until after receiving the results of the biopsies.

In the days prior to this the very clever and informative lemon campaign was launched. I realised then that I had more than one symptom. What a simple but effective way to get the message across. Why then do many of my friends look blank when I mention the campaign?

Prior to surgery I spread the word around my shocked friends and family, informing them of the various symptoms and stressing the benefit of regular checks. Many mammograms and prostrate tests were hastily booked. I was the last person they expected to succumb to this terrible disease. I have never smoked, I drank moderately, enjoy a healthy balanced diet, walk regularly and have an active outdoor lifestyle.

My main concern was for my daughter Sophie. Thankfully, as I was 58 years old, it was not considered to be genetic, despite my paternal grandmother, aunt and cousin having suffered from breast cancer. My daughter is sensibly breast aware. Unfortunately, breast cancer has no boundaries regarding age.

It was confirmed that I had three early stage tumours requiring a mastectomy and that several lymph nodes were also involved. A scan then revealed that the cancer was advanced and that I had secondary cancer in my bones. The shock was devastating. Through this dark terrifying time, it was the power of friendship that pulled me through.

Talking to close friends was a great comfort, for myself and for my husband. It reinforced the need for a positive outlook. When you are at your lowest point, it is those closest to you who will pick you up and give you the strength to carry on. I was also contacted by a friend of a friend who is a breast cancer nurse. This lady was invaluable in helping me to accept my situation and to cope with what was to come. She was a total stranger, but I could share with her my tears and innermost fears. I could discuss issues that I felt were too distressing to raise with even my husband or closest friends for fear of upsetting them. She had the experience and knowledge to really understand. I have met her since, and we are still in contact. To know that she is there whenever I feel the need to chat is such a comfort. Discussing your fears and feelings does help to ease the burden of this life changing diagnosis.

The most difficult conversation of all was breaking the news to my daughter. To learn that I had breast cancer was a huge blow. To be followed so quickly by the second diagnosis was shockingly cruel. We have had frank discussions since. Both of us accept that our lives will never be the same again but also that life must and will go on. We have chosen to continue as normal, living life to the full, enjoying each day, making happy memories, convinced that despite the odds, together we shall beat this.

It is a little discussed fact that over 30% of breast cancer patients will later develop advanced secondary cancer. Too painful to accept and even more so to talk about. This is so wrong. Conversation is essential. It promotes understanding of a difficult topic and allows those affected by this cruel disease, not just the cancer patient themselves but also their loved ones, to better appreciate the views and needs of everyone concerned. That way we can better support one another.

Juliet

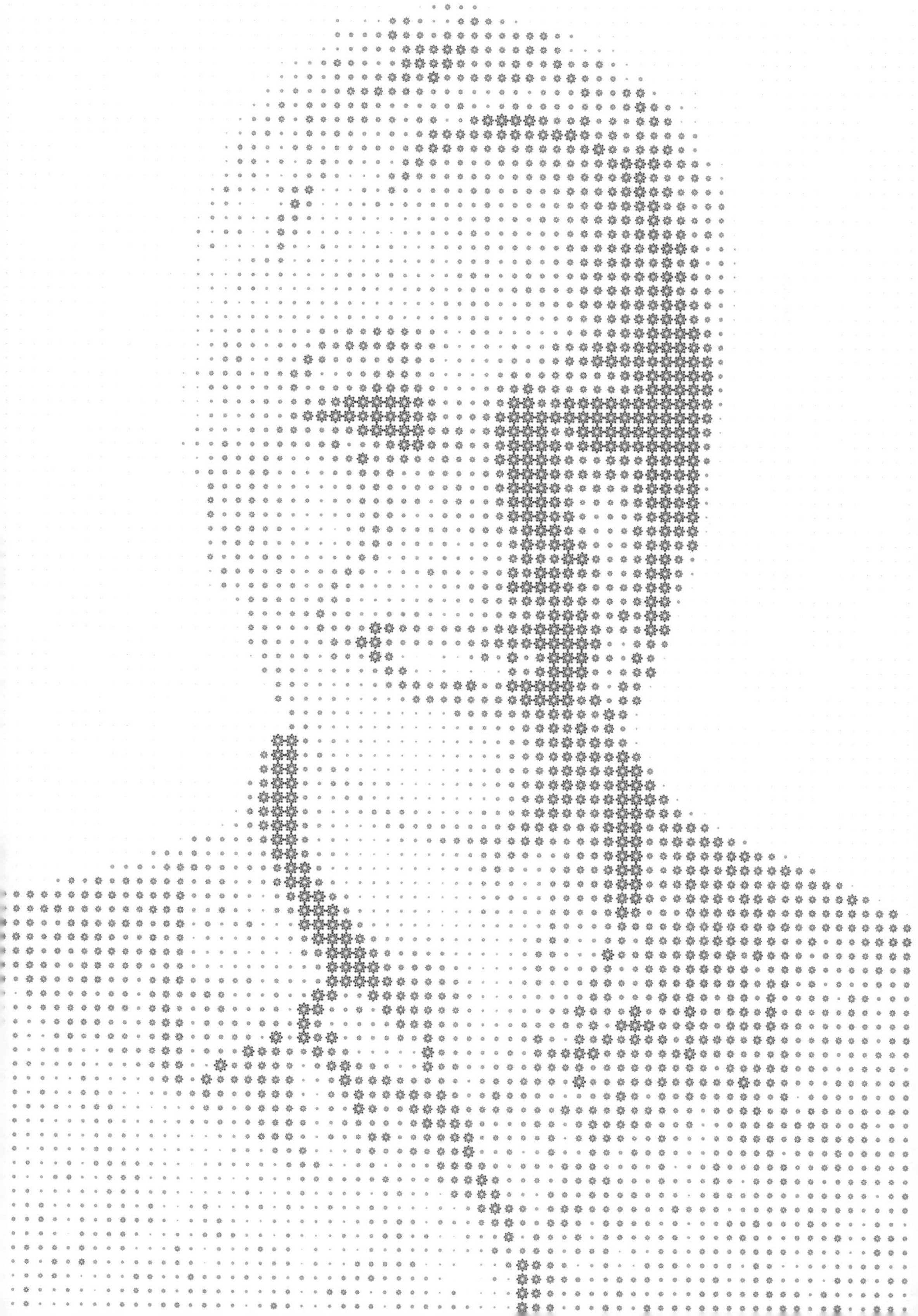

079

I was diagnosed in January 2015 with breast cancer, in my left breast, when I was 54 years old. It was after my second mammogram. I had no signs or symptoms and hadn't felt anything. So, it was a bit of a shock to say the least. After I found out, I got a lumpectomy, which is where they take a lump out of your breast to try and get rid of it that way. That wasn't enough, so I had to have a mastectomy. It was such a shock to me, and I was really upset about it. It had been one of my biggest fears for some reason, but it was fine. The operation was fine, and the lump was removed. I then had to have chemotherapy (four treatments all-together) and was on a drug that was injected into my leg every three weeks for a year. I lost all my hair, all over my body. I then was started on hormone drugs, but the first two types that I was given gave me awful side effects, so I am on a break from them to see what I am going to do about that.

After I had the mastectomy, I decided I wasn't going to have breast reconstruction because it was a really long operation – it can take up to eight or nine hours. So, I really didn't want that. I just wanted to get on with my life. The more I looked in the mirror as time went on, I realised I preferred looking at my scar on the left side, rather than my breast on the right. In the end I asked my surgeon to actually remove my other breast. It was size double-G and I wanted to be symmetrical. Eventually after 18 months he agreed he would do that surgery and when I woke up after that mastectomy, I immediately felt so much better. As time goes on, I have felt better and just more comfortable – I like my body a lot more. Plus, touch wood, I have no evidence of disease and I am cancer free at the moment.

When I got diagnosed, I didn't know anyone with breast cancer or anyone who had had breast cancer. Health care professionals told me that the most common and normal thing when diagnosed with breast cancer is to have a mastectomy and then to get reconstruction surgery. They showed me lots of photos of women after the surgeries. So, I automatically thought well that is what I have to do if that is what they are telling me. Initially I thought that I had to do that, but the more I looked into it the more I didn't want to have the operation. I then discovered a community of women on Facebook called Flat Friends. The women in this group are living without breasts or with one breast because they had decided not to have reconstructive surgery. One really interesting statistic I saw on the group that only 30% of women that have a mastectomy get reconstruction surgery. It was very surprising to me, due to what I had been told. Because of this, I am now trying very hard to bring awareness to this fact as well. I show my scars and talk to people about it, trying to de-stigmatise it. There are women out there that are now really happy and re-adjusted. They may miss their breasts a little, but they are completely getting on with their lives. It was great to discuss these things and it made me worry a lot less and actually feel empowered to do what I want to do. Being a part of Flat Friends helped keep me positive and I think that any social media platform is great. It makes such a difference to anyone with cancer.

A few months ago, I decided to have a photoshoot topless because I thought I was pretty beautiful without breasts and I wanted to have a record of that. Everyone on Flat Friends posts these kind of photos – photos of scars and problems or concerns we have about them. Quite a few people had put up their topless photos and it really made me want to do it. I was really lucky to have a friend who was a photographer, so we did the photos and they were amazing. I love them. Then I wanted to do something with them, rather than just have them sitting at home. So that's when I decided to start my blog, to tell my story and to share my photos. Because I hadn't known anyone with breast cancer and I thought if I can share my story it can help me, as well as other people. The response to my first post was just amazing. There were two or three women that were in the same position and said it helped them decide what to do.

This is an edited transcript of an interview between Helena Traill and Juliet on the 27th March 2019

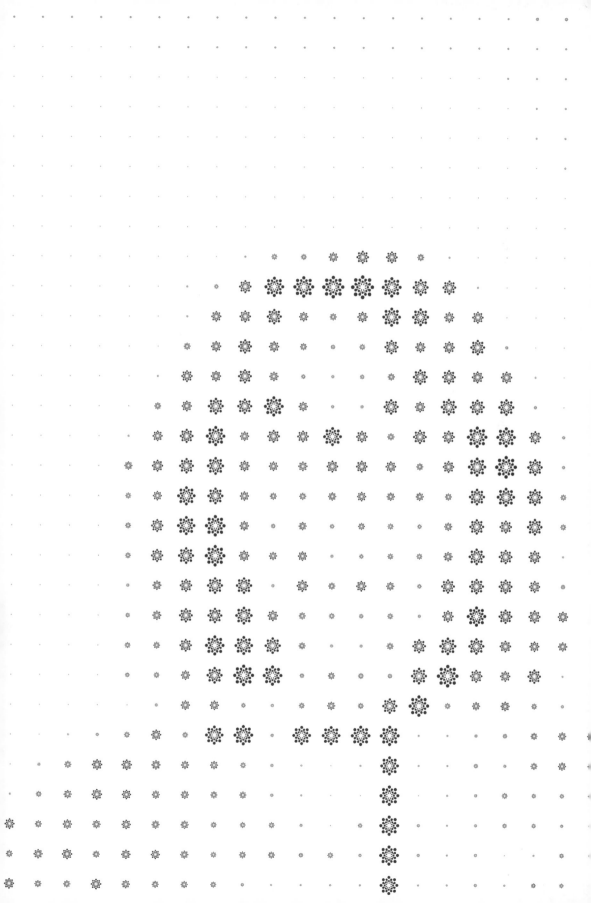

080

I have known deep down for the past 15 years or so that I would get breast cancer (an inward nag that I just couldn't shake), but when I found an indent in my right breast in October 2017, the writing was on the wall. I was immortal or so I thought, having led a healthy lifestyle for the 51 years I have been on this earth. Good diet, plenty of exercise, very little alcohol, never smoked, lean and fit and then my body goes and lets me down. How can I have been struck down by this thing? I always thought if it happened to me, I would cope. The question is: what is coping?

I continued to operate in a relatively normal kind of way (to an outsider at least), but to those close to me, they could see that coping was difficult. I continued to work throughout, against the advice of the medical staff, but the mortgage and all the bills still had to be paid. My mental health took a battering and now 18 months down the line I can look back and see the effect it had on me. I expected my body to bounce back and so had huge expectations and thought others were doing the same – which I couldn't live up to. Why didn't I have the strength to continue as before cancer – physically and mentally? I kept on asking that question. Another anxiety that was in the forefront of my mind, particularly at the beginning, was how are my family, husband and friends going to deal with it? What if I die, how will my they cope? That was hard. I used the word 'should' a lot – I should be feeling better, I should be able to work all day without getting tired, I should be able to get through one hour/day/week without collapsing in tears. That's what I kept telling myself and gradually, with help from my councillor and the Breast Cancer Care Moving Forwards Course I began to realise that the word 'should', should be banished.

Everyone is different, everyone copes differently and for me cancer brought out all those insecurities and vulnerabilities that I have lived with all my life but not necessarily expressed or dealt with. The deep-down disappointment of not achieving or making a difference to the world, even in a small way. The cancer was the final straw of a period of hard times and it nearly finished me off, mentally.

I was never one to talk about myself, my feelings or particularly mental health but since being diagnosed in October 2017 my attitude has changed. I now talk openly about my breast cancer, the pain, the fears, the ongoing fears and the fact that it takes you from a 'strong, capable, adaptable person' into a bedraggled mess in the corner of the room. But I talk about it for many reasons: to give strength to others that have or are going through it; that there is light at the end of the tunnel for us lucky ones; to show that it is not just a physical condition but an ongoing mental battle. Even though I am 'clear' of cancer, every ache and pain brings back that fear, that the cancer has returned in a different guise.

Not talking about it doesn't make it go away, so open conversation can help others be aware of:

1. The symptoms to look for.
2. How to support and be there for friends and family that are going through a cancer diagnosis or treatment.
3. What to say and what not to say.
4. The debilitating effect both mentally and physically that is related to cancer.
5. Just because I look 'fine' that doesn't mean I am.
6. The expectation that once treatment is over, everything is hunky dory – how wrong!

Unless someone tells you all of this, you can't be expected to know and therefore you don't know how to behave or cope, or what to even say. So open and honest conversation is important. However, it is easier said than done – I can sit here now and say these things but at the time when I was struggling I couldn't. The Breast Cancer Care Moving Forwards Course gave me the strength to believe that I was allowed to feel all those insecurities and that there was no expectation (I wasn't a lesser person because of it). Self-care is a saying that I never really understood but now I am an advocate of it, not just to cancer sufferers but to everyone. Unless you care for yourself by allowing yourself time (whether this is by reading a book, taking a jog, walking the dog, doing something spiritual), then no one else will. Let it become part of your everyday routine, so we all have time for ourselves – it is important. Make that time and learn what self-care works for you.

Emma

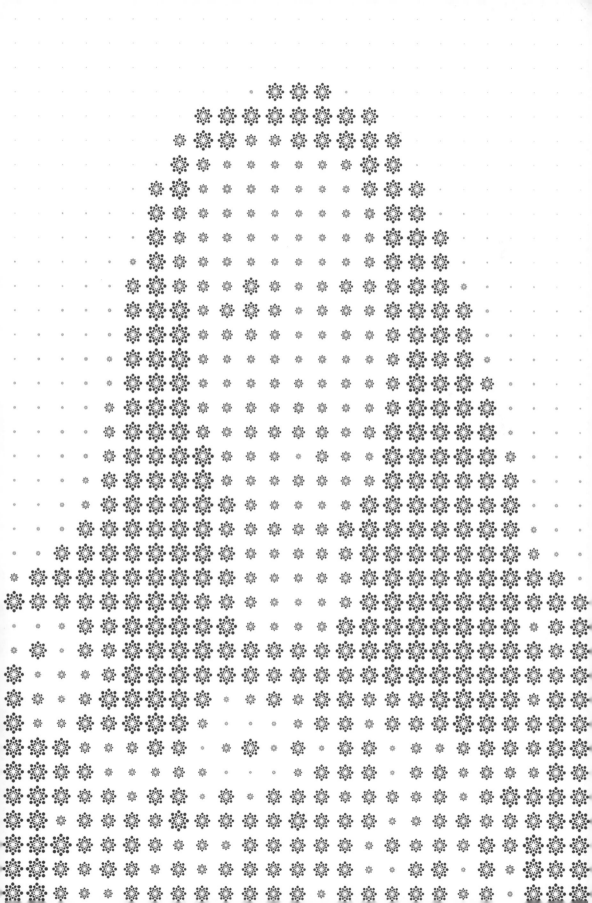

081

I was diagnosed in 2013 with cervical cancer. At the time I was 31 years old and it came completely out of the blue – out of nowhere. I first went to see my doctor and they thought something was wrong after the initial screening. After that I went to the hospital and the first thing they said was, 'You're incredibly young and I am not sure why you are here' and that was the start of my journey.

You generally associate the older generation with having cancer – my mum and my grandad had cancer. I don't know anyone around my age that had cancer, so I think I was diagnosed at a very young age. Before being diagnosed I actually missed my scheduled smear test the year before. It was actually the symptoms that prompted me to finally go. I had lost two stone in weight loss, had irregular bleeding, back and abdominal pain. Also Jade Goodie had recently passed away, from cervical cancer, so that was also in the back of my mind. If I hadn't gone for the test, then the diagnosis would have been a lot worse.

I didn't have the chemotherapy or radiotherapy, so I was fortunate to be able to keep my hair. I think going back to work after almost a year they wondered whether I had actually had cancer, as I still had my hair. I didn't have stares from not having hair, but I think I was judged for having hair. I felt like I had to justify what I had been through and the operations I had, numerous operations. Also, where I've had my lymph nodes removed in my groin it means I am not supposed to static stand for more than 20 minutes. So, having just come back from my honeymoon in Florida and standing in line at Disney Land, I just couldn't do it. We had to get special disability passes and, of course, I look normal – so then you get the stares, the looks and questions.

During my treatment I was so focused on going from one appointment to another, concentrating on getting better, that when I came out the other end, I remember thinking 'Well, what happens now?' – I felt emotionally different and felt left. I needed to do something or to access somebody who could give me support. My consultant pointed me in the direction of The Olive

Tree at Crawley Hospital. Through that I found Joe's Trust, which is a charity for cervical cancer and through that I met lots of people.

This was five years ago and to this day I still meet up with a few of them, they have become really good friends. It helps to know that what you are going through is 'normal' and to meet people that have had this in common with has helped so much. Not only for me, but for my husband as well, I wanted to be able to talk to other people that were going through something similar. So, it would feel normal, because at the time it did not feel normal. It was something that had brought us together and we could share our questions and concerns and have a conversation and just talk about it. I know with my husband he kept a lot bottled up, in order to help me and be strong for me. To begin with I think I was trying to protect him and trying not to talk to him too much about it. He then reached out to The Olive Tree and they supported him too, which then allowed him to help me.

It was also hard for friends to talk about it and really understand what was going on. I always made it very clear that they could ask me anything, because I knew being open would help them as well as me. What is scary is that a friend of mine was so scared when she found out I had cancer, as her only experience of cancer was death. We would talk about it lots and be so open, but to this day she has still not had a screening herself. Even after seeing what I have been through.

There is a Facebook group called Shine, which I joined and there is actually a group for people that have had the same specific operation that I have had. It is a very rare operation and is only available in particular parts of the country, so I'm part of that group too. When questions come up on that page and they are questions I feel I can answer, I respond to try and give advice. I'm not the best at getting online but it's more for me to help others than for me to ask questions. If I was being diagnosed now, I would reach out more on those groups, as social media is just always there. I didn't have so much support before my operation, it wasn't until after weeks and months after I thought, 'hang on a minute, I need some support from somewhere'. It's a lot easier and more accessible now but wasn't so much when I was going through it.

This is an edited transcript of an interview between Helena Traill and Emma on the 8th March 2019

Jonathan

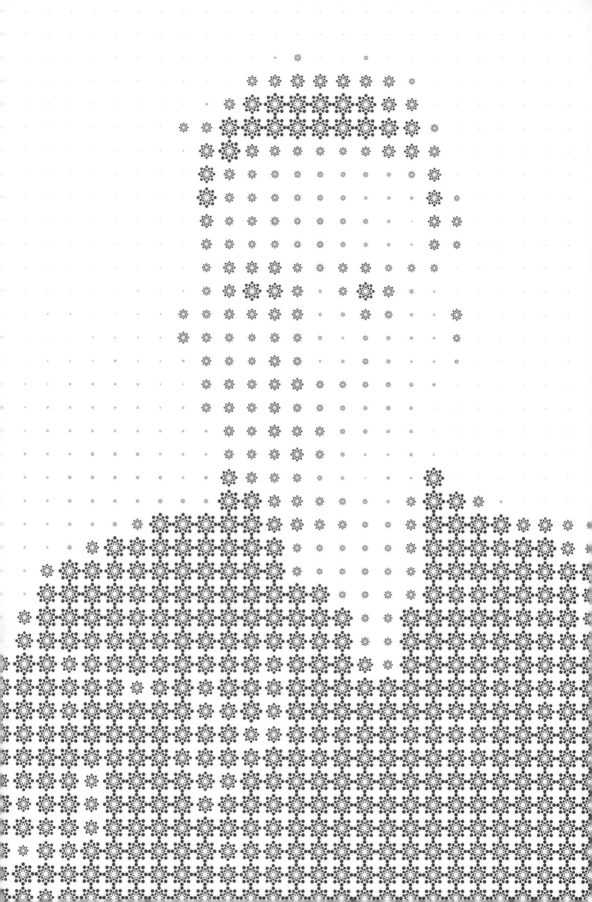

082

Following emergency brain surgery in 2007 (aged 25), after two years of chronic thirst and deteriorating eyesight, I was diagnosed with a malignant brain tumour (Pineal Germinoma) that had spread to my spine. Despite persistently seeing my doctor, she didn't initially recognise my symptoms, as I was a 'fit, healthy young man'.

With a year off work after surgery, for radiotherapy and treatment I felt my life was in limbo – getting through each day, coping with extreme fatigue, anxiety (caused by missing hormones due to damage to my adrenal and thyroid function) partial sight and mobility loss. My parents cared for me, doing everything for me at times. Despite losing my independence I have fond memories of how protected I felt and the time to appreciate the everyday things. Nature, art and writing helped my anxiety.

I still have yearly appointments and five yearly scans. My doctors are still doing tests to try and balance my hormones, which might help reduce my day-to-day fatigue and anxiety. I'm partially sighted due to a damaged optic nerve, which makes some things more difficult and I'm not permitted to drive. I use a white 'warning' cane that helps me get around. These ongoing effects do make me withdrawn, preferring to be alone. So, socialising and relationships can be difficult but, in the uptimes, I find ways to cope and strive on through the bad patches. To be made so aware of your mortality at a young age changes everything and coping with these effects, while friends steam ahead in life, with careers and families has made me feel I'm always playing catch up and it is a real test for my mental health too.

Open conversation is so important to help normalise the discussion, because it's only through talking and sharing what you're going through that you understand your own situation, the effect cancer's having on you physically and emotionally and how you are dealing with things. It helps to learn from others because you can see how they handle what they go through and this helps to share knowledge about your cancer type and treatment. In turn this can reduce concerns about what it will be like or to face it realistically, so you are better prepared. It helps to feel understood, that you're not the only one, for example, thinking every new pain is a new cancer or reacting unexpectedly when people say those well-meant clichés/wrong things or don't seem to understand what you're going through (that line, 'Well, we all face death eventually' or 'Any of us could have cancer').

Open conversation also helps wider society understand these things, the specific impacts cancer as a young adult has on life, physical and mental well-being and how to better respond to support people. This massively helps people facing it feel they can talk about their issues with anyone. The internet and social media has really allowed the discussion to open up and the reality of life with cancer to be better understood – that it doesn't automatically mean a death sentence and also the impact and struggles it creates in all aspects of life. It's helped people to share ways to get the most out of life in face of it and to see we're not abnormal in the things that happen to us, plus the way we think and feel. It's helped us all curse our situation but also laugh at some aspects of it, so that it has less power over every thought and we can feel as normal as possible despite all the prodding, poking and dark moments, that we never knew would be part of life (so early on in case of younger adults). It helps us shout out about what we need, to advocate to health services about things that can be done better and for friends/family to see when we need them. It's connected strangers to have each other's back, through it all, and can give you that instant motivational comment you need. The biggest thing is the access to information and advice, though equally the danger is that we are advised incorrectly or unhelpfully, which is why finding reliable organisations online is so important too.

And that's where organisations like Shine Cancer Support help. I found Shine in 2017 after leaving my job in London, realising the lasting effects of my cancer meant that I couldn't cope as well with a high-pressure job. I'd moved down to the sea for a calmer life, closer to family and got a place on Shine Great Escape. This amazing retreat connected me with other young adults, who all understood what each other were going through and the sessions gave us all ways to cope living life with all cancer's thrown. I now work with Shine as Communication and Fundraising Officer, helping ensure everyone knows our support is there for them. Our online resources, regular get-togethers and workshops help with issues like working with cancer, anxiety or life-coaching. All our support is here to make things easier, so that no one is alone.

Nicola

083

I've had two cancers in the last three years. My journey started in November 2016 and continues to this day. I was diagnosed with endometrial cancer in November 2016 aged 40. I had a radical hysterectomy (removal of the womb, ovaries and cervix) and was given the all clear in January 2017. Unfortunately, cancer wasn't done with me yet and I had a reoccurrence in November 2018. This time I needed radiotherapy and brachytherapy (internal radiotherapy) which finished six weeks ago. I am still awaiting results to see if I am in remission again. For years I was told I was too young for this type of cancer or my heavy bleeding was normal or sent away with yet another pill to limit the effects – instead of finding the problem. This is why I have openly shared my cancer journey on social media via Facebook. Communication is vital.

Physically I feel like I'm broken. My body has let me down spectacularly, it can't give me the child I longed for. I do not trust it. I am left with fatigue (imagine swimming through a vat of treacle). The side effects impact every aspect of my life, my job, the things I enjoy doing, my relationships, the way I see myself as a person. It has shattered my confidence and my self-esteem. Emotionally I can only describe it as a roller-coaster that you want to get off. You skip from fear to anxiety, disappointment or guilt. You mourn the person you once were and the life you once had. But that's all mixed up with some amazing moments of hope, faith, positivity, fight and love. The things that were once important no longer are, but the people who support, nurture and in effect save you, make you remember the reason you're getting up in the morning and facing the world.

Endometrial cancer is a difficult topic for some people. Women, especially older women, don't always talk openly about their periods or their 'lady bits' and it's often a taboo subject. It's vital we change this mind set and call a spade a spade, or a vagina a vagina. For years I wasn't taken seriously by medical professionals because I was 'too young' or it was just 'woman's problems'. Had I discussed this more openly with other women I would have known how far from normal my situation was and fought harder for a diagnosis. I've talked openly throughout my journey as communication promotes awareness and awareness saves lives. I manage a mental health service and am very much aware of how vital good mental health is. Cancer is a scary and isolating place. You can be in a room full of people and unless you are talking (and someone is actually listening) it can be the loneliest place on earth. The range of emotions a cancer diagnosis brings can be frightening for the people close to you, they don't know what to say or do – cancer is taboo. Some of them inevitably disappear when you need them most, these are the ones that don't know how to communicate their fears.

Talking promotes good mental health but it's about asking the right questions, the important questions, the taboo questions. Communication strengthens relationships. Talking about cancer should be as easy as talking about having a cold. Without good open communication it is impossible to support someone effectively or meet their holistic needs.

My entire journey has been and will continue to be shared on Facebook. Everyone I know is now aware of the symptoms of endometrial cancer. On average, I'd say 50% of my Facebook friends are women, the other 50% have wives, daughters, grandmother's, aunties, nieces or female friends. If one-person sees a post and recognises a symptom and shares this with a loved one, then they may be diagnosed at an earlier stage when the cancer is curable. Social media promotes open communication. I live in a small village and everyone knows I'm, 'the lady with womb cancer'. I'm good with that. When I first went public, I was overwhelmed by the number of private messages to ask about symptoms or to share stories or just tell me that is exactly how they feel right now. At each stage I've updated everyone (other than family of course) via social media. Sometimes you don't have the strength to repeat the conversation many times, this reaches a large audience in a short space of time. I am also active on a number of support forums and have written a couple of blogs. I have supported other women who are at earlier stages of their journey, just as other ladies supported me when I was scared and vulnerable. These people have no faces, so I can tell them what I like, and they will not judge me – I don't know them other than their cancer story, yet they are a huge part of my day. Without social media this wouldn't be possible.

Cancer is scary but by talking about the treatment, the side effects, the emotional turmoil, the struggle with fear, it makes it less taboo and makes people feel less alone and isolated.

Judy

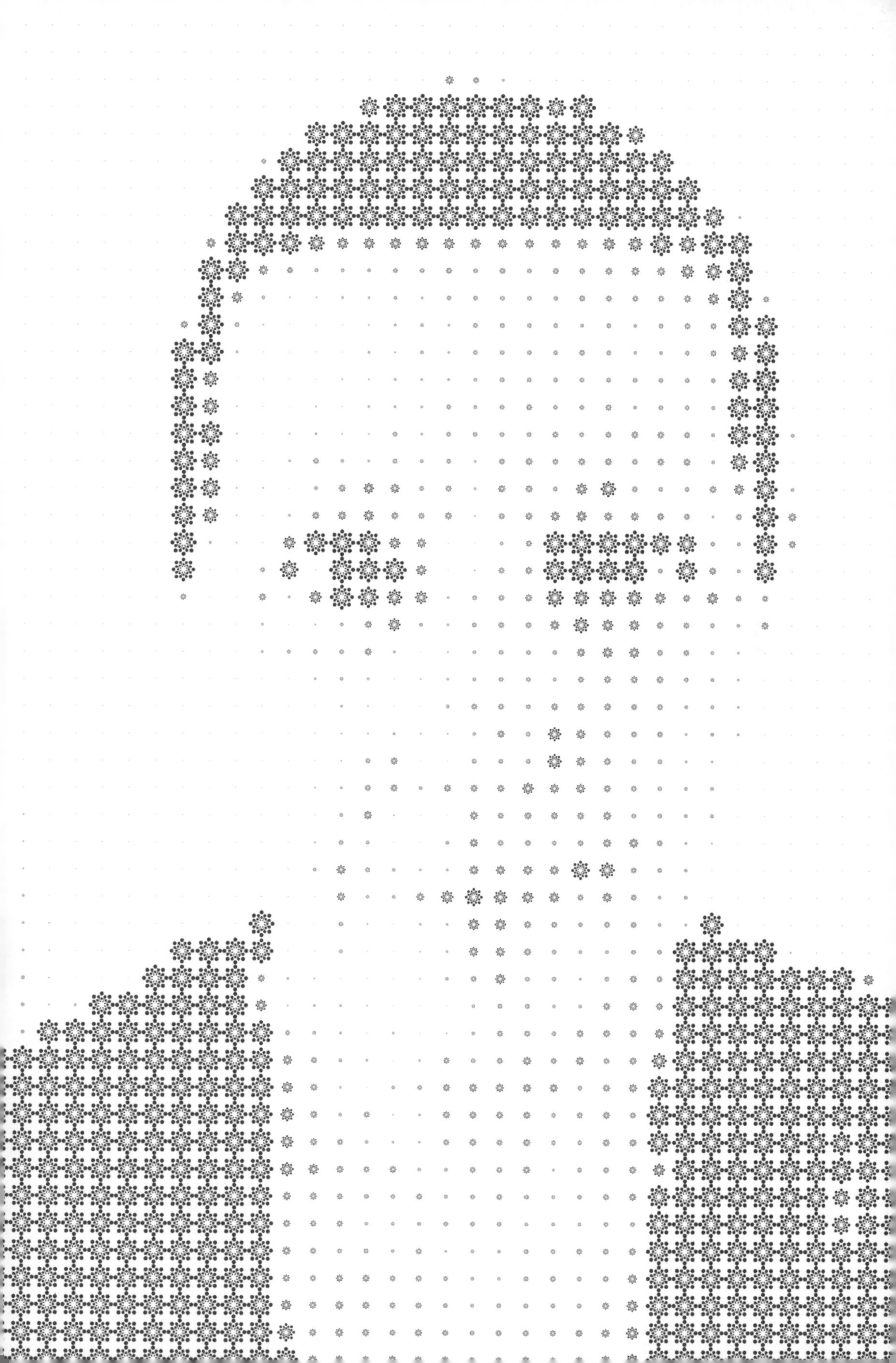

084

I don't see cancer in terms of how it has affected me, instead I am more aware of the impact the treatment has had an impact on my day-to-day life. As a bit of background, I had breast cancer which was picked up during a standard three yearly mammogram. Two small tumours caught very early, no lymph node involvement and I was not aware of any lumps. So, stage 1 but an aggressive HER2+ type grade 3 cancer. At diagnosis I was otherwise a fit and healthy 56-year-old. I have never felt that I had cancer. For me, because it was a stage 1 tumour and there were proven treatment options, the cancer diagnosis didn't feel like a death sentence. Saying that I've started knocking holidays off my bucket list – I have just been to Mexico in March and I am going to Santorini in September. Live for today.

It is very hard for your friends and family because unfortunately they do not fully understand – how can they if they've not been through it? My dad had two different cancers over a 15-year period. Looking back, it's just like a bad dream.

After the lumpectomy in June 2019 my five year survival rates were 75% and after having six cycles of chemotherapy (July to November 2019), 15 radiotherapy sessions which finished on Christmas Eve, ongoing three weekly Herceptin injections for a year and an ongoing daily Bisphosphonates tablets for three years, my odds have improved to 85%. Some people may think that the treatment isn't worth the extra 10% but I like to think I've given myself every chance. Don't get me wrong, in the back of my mind I know there is a chance of secondary cancer, but my odds are good.

My place of work was brilliant, whilst undergoing treatment. I had six months off work but did complete a few hours at home when I felt okay. I also called into the office several times for brief visits to keep in touch, so I didn't feel isolated. In some ways, cancer treatment has expanded my life, I've gained lots of knowledge, have met some lovely people and it has made me a little more appreciative of the smaller things.

If I'm honest, I felt shocking through most of the chemotherapy, but the hair loss was probably the worst part of it – knowing it will grow back doesn't actually make you feel any better about losing it. Maybe I should have tried the scalp cooling but I can't bear being cold so I really don't think I could have tolerated it. Plus, you still lose your eyebrows, eyelashes and the other less visible hair. I haven't bawled my eyes out over the diagnosis or the treatment, but my hair growing back slower than I'd like does make me shed an odd tear and feel a bit sorry for myself on occasions – although I do have a fab wig.

I've been back at work full time since February and have found that my concentration levels are much lower, and my memory is pretty poor – good old chemo brain. On bad days I have the niggling thought that maybe I can't do my job properly but then again am I expecting too much of myself too soon? Only time will tell.

Open conversation is very important. I've been very honest and have been happy to discuss my diagnosis with anyone. I think in the early days people didn't like to ask, in case they upset you and they didn't want to look like they were prying. Although a lot of people have a 'cancer story', generally they are at opposites end of the spectrum – the person with cancer either died or breezed through it. Neither are particular helpful, although I'm sure they mean well. I believe that the more conversations that are had around cancer should help to reduce the fear factor, improve knowledge of warning signs and encourage people (particularly men) to go and get a problem checked out. I wanted to devour everything about breast cancer as I felt that knowledge was power.

I didn't google indiscriminately, I used Breast Cancer Care, Macmillan and Cancer Research. I joined the chemotherapy monthly thread forum on Breast Cancer Care – this was great for discussing side effects and feeding off people in a similar position. I started listening to You, Me & The Big C podcast – fantastic, I can't praise this podcast enough. I've laughed and cried listening to this and it's been great that the media picked up on it. When Rachael Bland died, I felt like I'd lost a friend. Through social media I came across Liz O'Riordan book about breast and Deborah James' book about her bowel cancer story. In fact, I initially saw your details through Liz' twitter account.

I read loads of blogs and this encouraged me to venture into that area. So, I decided to write a blog, Dancing With Chemo, for several reasons:

1. As therapy for me, because if you write it down I think you are more accepting of the situation and it clears your mind a little.

2. Writing a blog is great in the middle of the night when you feel rubbish but can't sleep due to a steroid buzz, it's like talking to someone who understands.

3. Rather than have to talk (and repeat myself) to lots of individuals, I posted my blog on Facebook and Twitter so my friends, distant family, colleagues and acquaintances would know where I was in the medical process and how I was coping.

People really did appear to find it useful and the feedback and support was lovely, so it did help a lot.

Bill

085

Shortly after my diagnosis I went onto WebMD (an American website that publishes information pertaining to human health and well-being) to read about it. None of my doctors told me that 95% of the people who have what I have, at the stage I have it, are dead within five years of the diagnosis. Social media did though. My first goal was to be in the 5%, who are still alive five years later, and that actually looks likely to me now.

Anyway, my name is Bill Werther, and when I started seeing blood in my urine, I ended up meeting some urologists, and oncologists and went into their world. I found having stage 4, muscle invasive, metastatic bladder cancer has been an eye opening, and mostly positive experience for me. Not to say I am glad that I have it, but it has helped me grow as a human being, and for that, I am grateful. Cancer has been positive for me in that: I appreciate being alive, because I no longer just take it for granted. My perspective on what is important in my life got its ass kicked with the diagnosis, I am so much better because of the cancer. I am much better at determining if there is something I can do about a problem, and if not, then I let it go easily, and I do it much better than the pre-cancer diagnosis Bill ever did.

The 'Bill with cancer' doesn't let things I can't control stress me out at any level near how that pre-diagnosis Bill did. Because of the diagnosis, I have developed a mental strength I did not have prior to the diagnosis. Cancer has helped me quit some bad habits, start some good habits, but it took some time to get to that mind set. I had to struggle through nine months of chemotherapy. I felt sorry for myself for a few months after the diagnosis, I lost a bunch of billable hours for my work, depleted my savings while running up credit cards as well, I worried more about failing my children as a provider than I ever did about dying. I was so worried the cancer would cause me to lose my income and fall out of the middle class, but after being diagnosed in November 2016, going through a rough patch mentally, by the summer of 2017 I felt like I had gotten back up off the floor, and the shock of getting knocked down in the first place changed me for the better. My first cancer doctor got me into a clinical trial, and I have been doing well in that program. The drug they have me on appears that it will get FDA approval and the last five scans have all been very positive. I could go on, but you asked for 'a paragraph' and here we are six paragraphs deep.

My experience has been that having cancer is not as devastating as I had previously imagined it, prior to my diagnosis. After a little bout with depression and a personal pity party, shortly after discovering it got me, I began talking about it with my teenage children in a positive way – not because I was positive, but because I did not want to have a negative attitude around them. I did not want them to worry over something they had no control over. In essence I was faking it, but the old adage 'fake it til' you make it' has some truth in it. I'm not sure exactly when I started believing I was going to live the five years, but I truly believe it now. Conversation was the tool that changed that mindset for me. Conversation is created first by thoughts, thoughts become words, sentences, paragraphs, and soon the energy of the words and conversation effect your outlook or attitude. Your attitude and outlook create who we are as people, so I am a proponent of a more normalised and less stigmatised attitudes towards what it means to be diagnosed with cancer. There are lots of sucky things about having cancer, but nothing has been as eye opening an experience in all of my 53 years of living either. Having lived most of my life believing there was nothing good about having cancer, only to find there are lots of positives too, I realised it was kind of a taboo subject for me. My assumptions were wrong.

Social media is a lot of things, both negative and positive, but having cancer has humbled me, it has also helped me connect with other people better than pre-diagnosis Bill was capable of doing. Having cancer just makes you care so much less about what other people may be thinking about you, or judging you, because it creates such a focus on what is really important in life. The internet has become more alive because I no longer have as much worry about putting something on the web that's just stupid. Go ahead, mock me on the internet, but I still love you! The connectedness social media provides has helped me meet some fascinating people online as well. I created a cancer list on my Twitter account, and I add people that have cancer and also oncologists and urologists. I am able to read about the science of cancer, on the internet. That has helped me understand how others perceive cancer, because other people's stories on the internet can also be inspiring.

Sal

086

I was first diagnosed with breast cancer in 2013, at the age of 36. I am married and my two boys were just five and eight at the time. It came as a massive shock. They say everyone knows someone who has cancer but at my age, I did not, and cancer was a big taboo subject in the Asian community – no one ever talked about it. I was extremely scared; I didn't know much about treatment or outcomes and the first few weeks were very tough. I connected with people online and joined the Young Breast Cancer Network which is a private Facebook group. I asked all the questions and had an immense amount of support. I had chemotherapy, surgery and radiotherapy and nine months later I was cured of my cancer. I decided to put it all behind me and move on with my life.

Just three years later, I had a niggling pain in my knee. I went to my doctor who sent me for a blood test. My results came back and showed that my liver enzymes were extremely elevated and there was a suspicion that I had cancer again. This came totally out of the blue. How did I manage to get cancer for the second time? Investigations began and went on for 10 months until I was finally diagnosed with the extremely rare and dangerous bile duct cancer. I knew I had survived one cancer, but I didn't know if it was possible to survive a second. There was and is so much information about breast cancer, so much support, treatment, over 50 charities, I felt lost and scared. I started to do my research and found another Facebook group for patients with Cholangiocarcinoma and again, I had found my support network.

In October 2018, I was scheduled to have a liver resection to remove the lesion in my bile duct. Once in theatre, my surgeon saw that my cancer had metastasized to my liver and stomach lining. I was now stage 4 and had to start chemotherapy. I started to write a blog. I found this to be very therapeutic and a release for me. My blog started to reach people in other countries and within a month I had over 1000 views in 33 countries. This inspired me to keep writing and sharing my story. I have connected with so many people who have bile duct cancer and it seems it is not so rare and affects many younger people too.

I did eight months of chemotherapy – it was harsh, and the drugs took a massive toll on my body. People keep asking me, if I am done and I have finished now. With a stage 4 cancer, there is no definite plan, it is a step-by-step approach and each scan determines the next step. After my chemotherapy finished, my scans unfortunately showed that the cancer had spread to my lymph nodes. I am now on second line of treatment which is more targeted for the receptors on my cancer cells.

I do not wear my cancer on the outside. I don't live with cancer, but cancer lives with me. I get out as much as I can and connect with other patients and it is a massive support network for all to pull each other through the hard times. I think that a lot of people struggle behind closed doors especially in the Asian community and there is so much support out there. Cancer is not always the end and you need to take control and fight it every step of the way. I have good weeks and bad weeks. It has not been an easy ride. In fact, the second time around has been quite tough, however, I do try and get out as much as I can and use it as a distraction.

When I go out, I do not like to talk about my cancer and explain every detail to my friends and family. Everything is written in my blog. It is my witty account of my journey in the most unfortunate circumstances. It is an honest and frank account of what happens week-to-week, told in my own quirky way. My blog has now reached 66 countries around the globe and I feel like I am connected with the world. I have had many patients connect with me and we share our treatment journeys and coping mechanisms with each other. You can become friends with a complete stranger and have such a strong bond when you are connected by cancer. It is a really useful tool and if I am having a really hard time and not managing at home, my friends who are following my blog will message and turn up with food for the family without me having to call around and ask for help.

I recently organised a 12-hour walking relay, to raise funds for the only charity in the UK dedicated to bile duct cancer, AMMF charity. I wasn't sure how the day would go or even if I would be well enough, but I had over 150 supporters join me. This included friends, family, colleagues and teachers and staff from my son's school. We had many people take part, for every hour of the day and from start to finish. The weather was amazing, and we raised £5500 in just one day. I was really pleased with my efforts – when I can't I don't but when I can I really do.

I find that channelling my energy and efforts from negative to positive keeps me going every day. It is not easy living with a stage 4 cancer, but I think I am doing okay. It is what you make of it. I choose life – I create memories with my children, I travel, take photos, meet with my friends and do all those things that make me happy. I don't have the energy to cry or the time to crumble. Life is precious and there is not a day that goes by without that thought in my head. I am now one year on after being diagnosed with my second cancer and am living my best life, every day I can.

Martino

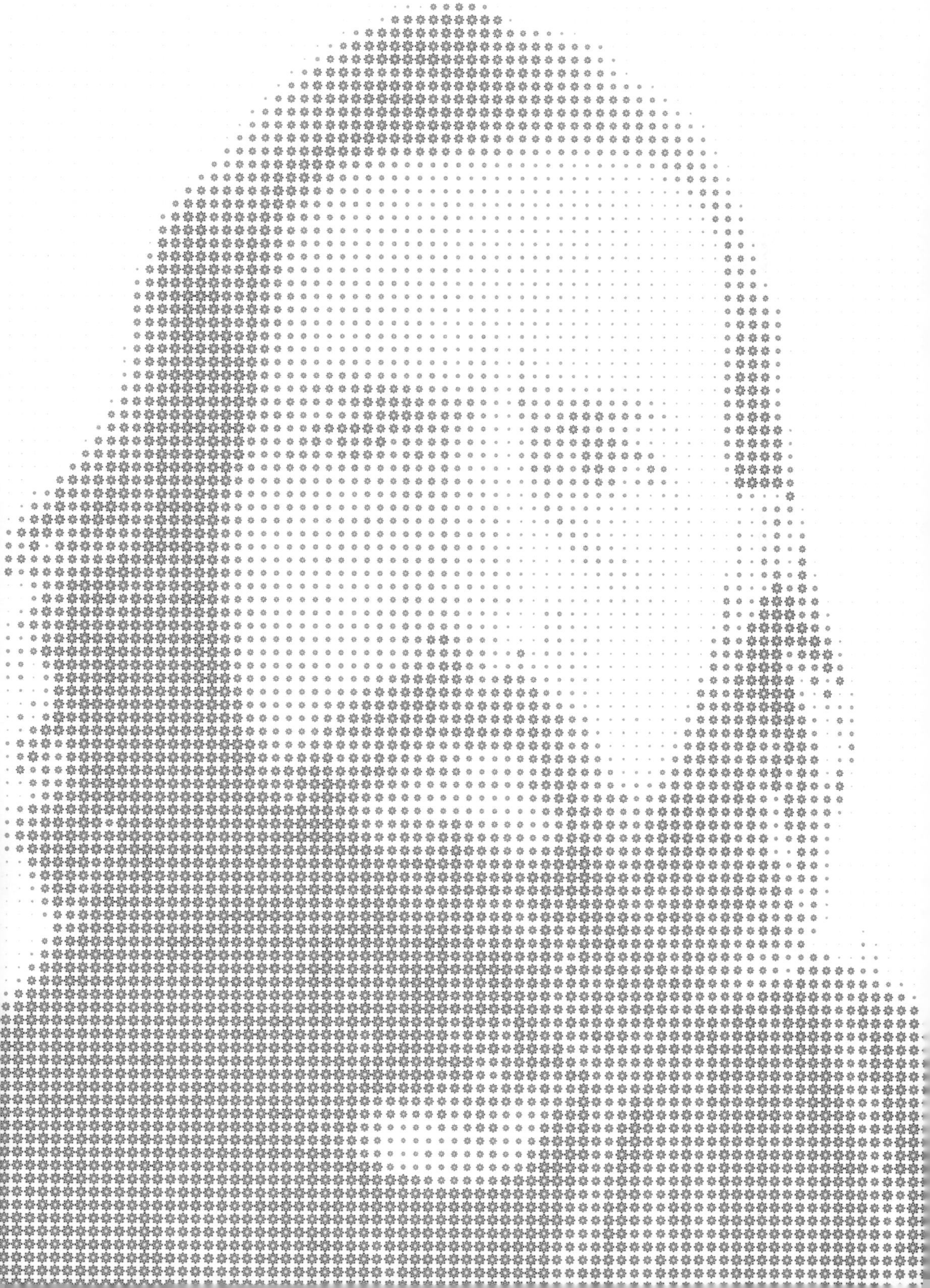

087

After the last operation on my brain I woke up – I had the same surgeon who had opened up my brain the first time and I am still alive, so I thought, 'Okay, I will have him again'. He's one of those people who doesn't really speak too much, he just said, 'Well, you only have six months of your life, so let me just try and get all of it out'. A lot of other doctors were very scared of cutting away too much, which would lead me to being handicapped. It was pretty scary to be told that maybe I wouldn't be able to speak in any language, at all.

I had a good friend of mine there with me, an English lady. I have always hung out with comedians. She was there to keep me company and put me in a good mood. I tried speaking English but when I woke up I just couldn't. I couldn't understand what other people were saying. It took me weeks to get my Italian back and once I had a little bit of that, I then got my English back.

My German friend, he only calls me in German (he hangs out here in London all the time and can speak perfect English, but we only speak German with each other), he actually forced it and you know it did actually come back. Of course, I feel a little more handicapped than before, but at least I can talk.

I understand that for a lot of people it is very difficult to speak about illness in general. I think in England they know that there are active groups of people that can come together and talk about their problems and decide to actually do something, as a group. I think it's just radical and it means the whole family is actually doing something and talking about it. I've noticed in Italy and other countries that most families just feel helpless and wonder what they can do. They are home with this person that is perhaps a little handicapped and they can't do anything about it. You yourself have to be active and actually do something. For me, it was writing a book, in a way, because I can't really work much because my brain doesn't work very well. So, for me, yes, writing a book seemed impossible – while not being able to read or remember what I've just written, it would be impossible. But, having the calm of people around me allowed me to slowly do it. It took years to do it. I then met a lot of writers who tell me that writing in general is very difficult – but for me a bit more so, as I have to remember what I've just typed away.

Writing my own egocentric story about myself and my life, I can't say I was that convinced that it would be very interesting for the people. But actually, it turned out that a lot of people, like my friends, would read the bits I was writing and get very excited about it. So again, you can narrate and talk about it with people, but I wanted to use the drama in some kind of fun way. Ultimately, I realised that what I was writing was actually useful for me, it was definitely healthy for me to narrate it. I found some irony in my own life – it was very helpful. It also helped my family a lot, because they realised I was actually in a good mood and not depressed.

I realise for a lot of people it would be a very depressing thing. When I go to doctors to show them the MRI's it's just big holes and big parts of the brain that have been moved away. I looked at it and saw that the big hole looked like a finch. It was so useful to have that relationship, because rather than having a big evil thing in my head it was nicer to narrate that scary thing and have a relationship with a bird that was in there. Otherwise I might think it was a big evil thing that wanted to attack me. So, by finding a way of narrating it to myself it has been very comforting.

I myself don't really socialise very much. I am conscious that for a lot of normal lives they have problems themselves, but they don't seem so important because for me just being alive and staying alive is my priority. I don't want to tell a person in their 'normal life' when they ask what I do 'I just take life day by day'. So, I do have a vision and a lot of us have a vision that every day has to be a beautiful day, and that we have to appreciate every single day because we could be dying tomorrow. That's just the nature of living, that is just how you do it.

It is socially very difficult to listen to people say things like, 'My kids are not going to the really posh school'. Is that a real problem? I completely understand that this is their reality and I am not going to be critical about it but, for me, being alive is difficult. My priorities are so different. I have to find a way to narrate things with a type of humour so that people can accept it and we can start ways of talking about normal problems of normal lives. Mine are different, you know, and it's okay but very tricky and complex. We all have to work on that together, that includes my family and friends. We just have to normalise it and get them to say, 'Oh Martino, he has a hole in his head'.

My kid who is 11 years old now, he speaks to his friends about it, which I think is very cool. He is a very healthy kid and I can talk to him about getting another MRI scan by saying, 'You know the machine that goes burh burh burh'. So, one has to find ways to talk to kids – it is what it is, and it is ok. It doesn't need to be so dramatic; we are here and every day is a beautiful day. That is it.

This is an edited transcript of an interview between Helena Traill and Martino on the 13th March 2019

Julia

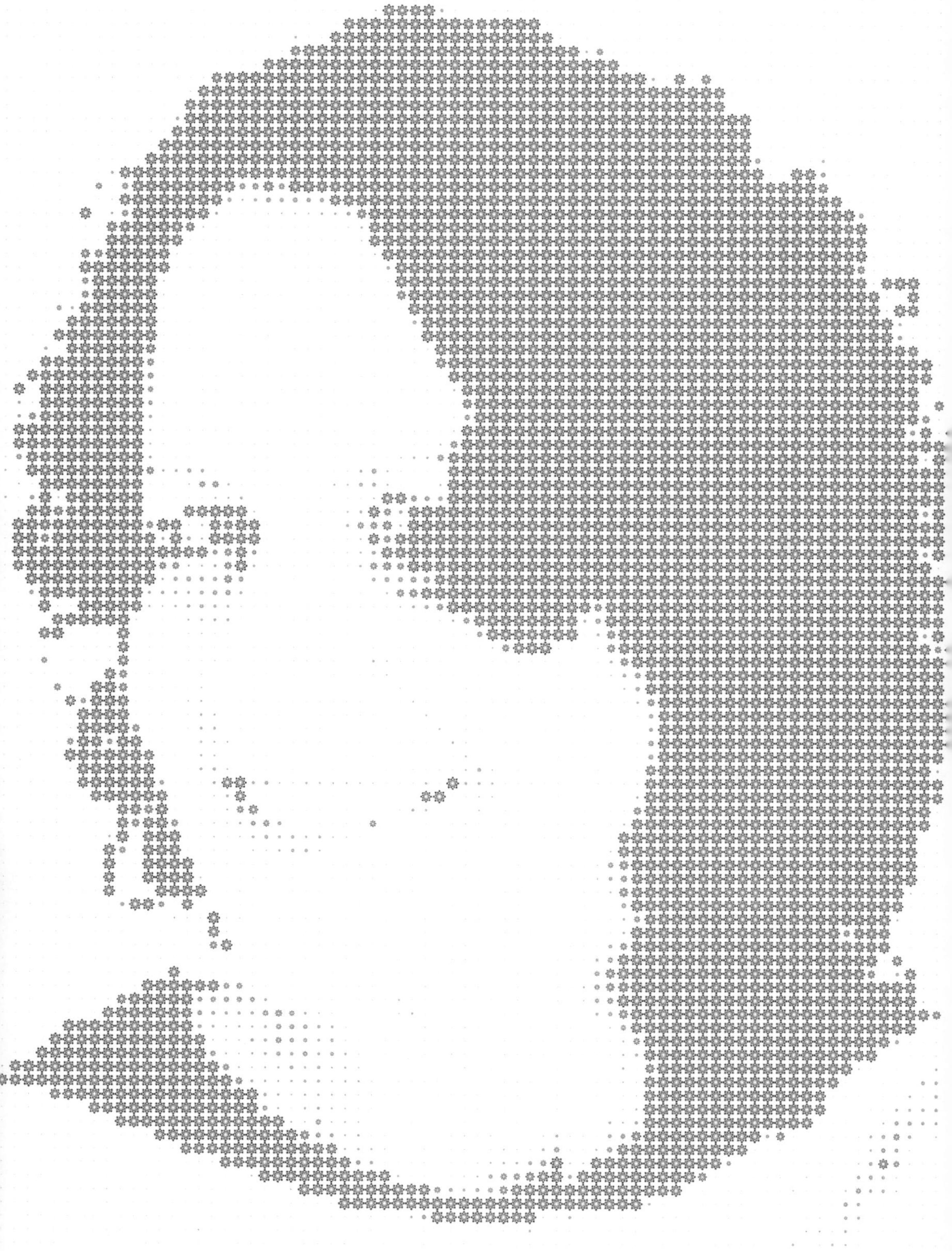

088

Everyone is different. We have different cancers, different treatments and different experiences of those treatments. I think it is important we can be open, share and talk about our cancer experiences to raise awareness and understanding. This in turn encourages others to get checked and to give and receive support. Social media is a great way of meeting other people and it helps give our experiences meaning and a voice. This is about my experiences. This is my cancer story.

We were busy getting ready for Christmas and our daughter's wedding. I tried on my wedding outfit, including my new underwear. Just before putting on my new bra I decided to do a quick breast check and it was then that I noticed a lump in my breast. I didn't have time to give it much thought and rationalised that it was unlikely to be breast cancer. I had a healthy lifestyle and having recently celebrated my 48th birthday was relatively young. I put it to the back of my mind and enjoyed Christmas and the wedding.

A few weeks later my husband, son and I were on holiday in Cornwall celebrating my husband's 50th birthday. We were enjoying bracing cliff top walks and cosy fireside pub meals. One day I brushed my hand against my breast and noticed the lump again. It had changed, it was bigger and felt gnarly. I thought maybe I was imagining it but when husband felt it, he was concerned too. I booked the next available appointment with my doctor which was about two weeks away.

Once we were back home, I started thinking about people I knew who had been diagnosed with cancer, some who had died, including family and friends. After a few days I was feeling so worried I made an urgent same day appointment to see a nurse practitioner who examined me and made an urgent referral to the breast clinic.

At the breast clinic, a breast care nurse examined me. I had a mammogram and an ultrasound before seeing a consultant who explained that my results weren't conclusive – so I needed a biopsy. The results from the biopsy suggested I had a grade 0 ductal carcinoma in situ (DCIS). It needed to be removed but my prognosis was extremely good. The plan was for surgery followed by radiotherapy and a date was arranged for a wide local excision about two weeks later. My surgery went well and soon life was getting back to how it had been before. When I saw the consultant for my pathology results, I was told that it was very bad news. The lump they removed contained an aggressive, fast growing grade 3 invasive cancer in addition to the grade 0 DCIS. I was told I would need more surgery to check whether the cancer had spread to my lymph nodes, followed by chemotherapy and targeted therapy as well as the radiotherapy already planned. It felt surreal. When the news sunk in, I sobbed like never before. As a wife, mother, daughter, sister, sister-in-law, auntie, niece and friend I wanted to protect those around me from this life changing news, but I couldn't. I couldn't protect myself either.

Even though I knew people who'd been diagnosed with breast cancer I didn't know much about it. I felt confused by the all the medical terminology and decided to educate myself. I looked at the Breast Cancer Now website. I hadn't realised that there are many types and sub-types of breast cancer and that treatments are so varied.

I wanted to connect with others affected by breast cancer. I found the dedicated forums quite overwhelming, so I had a look on Twitter. I like the brevity of tweets and the speed at which I can scroll through them deciding if and when to read them and interact with others. When searching for #breastcancer, I soon came across an amazing community of people with experience of breast cancer and other cancers who became an incredible source of information and support. There was always someone somewhere to talk to, even in the middle of the night.

I was shocked how ill chemotherapy made me. A week after my first infusion I developed a high fever and, after calling the dedicated oncology helpline, I had my first emergency admission to hospital. Most of the people I was sharing a hospital room with were much older than my parents. I felt completely out of place. After a couple of days, I was discharged but within a week I developed another high fever and this time I was diagnosed with neutropenic sepsis, which is a life-threatening condition. I was so ill I needed to be isolated for my own protection.

My scalp was tender because my hair was falling out. I had excruciating headaches and couldn't bear any light. My mouth and throat were covered in mouth ulcers. I had a revolting metallic taste in my mouth. I was incredibly thirsty. The scar under my arm, which had healed, started opening up again. My blood pressure and heart rate were extremely high. My stomach was sore, and my back, pelvis and legs were really painful. I was scared I might die there and then but with the intravenous antibiotics and fluids I pulled through. I'll never forget the kindness of some of the staff I met during that hospital stay.

As I continued with chemotherapy, I kept becoming ill with fevers and my husband became my carer. I had a lot of unplanned visits to hospital, often in the middle of the night, and developed neutropenic sepsis again. When the decision was made that it was too dangerous for me to have my final chemotherapy, I felt relieved – my body felt broken. I needed help with basic tasks like washing, walking and so on. After my heart function was checked, my targeted therapy resumed, and I had radiotherapy (which was better than expected).

Since finishing treatment two years ago I've been learning to manage the ongoing effects, such as fatigue and pain as well as all the menopausal symptoms brought on suddenly by my chemotherapy induced menopause. I've been slowly processing all that has happened, and I've been making a new life for myself. The twitter community has continued to be an enormous support. I know I am not alone.

Alexandra

089

My cancer diagnosis was in January 2010. I was a super healthy person. I didn't smoke, I didn't drink much, I was fit and healthy, but I did get cancer and the first woman in my family to get cancer. I was 45 years old and I found a lump in my breast, I didn't think it was anything and I was five years away from screening. I wasn't actually going to do anything about it, because it was around Christmas and I was working at a primary school. It was all carol concerts and glitter. It was actually my then-husband who had encouraged me to go and get it checked. I got it checked and within two weeks I was seen, and I had a mammogram followed by a deep core biopsy (which is where they put a needle in to the breast to take a bit of the lump out). Then I was immediately shown into a consulting room.

I knew it wasn't good news because beside the consultant was a Macmillan nurse. I hadn't even taken my husband; my friend had driven me and was waiting outside. I was on my own in there. He then said I am 99% sure that it is cancer, but we will have to wait two weeks to confirm this. It was at that point I burst into tears and all I heard was, 'Blah blah blah'. As I was leaving, I was wondering why there was a box of tissues upside down by the door. Two weeks came and went, we didn't tell anybody. At the time my son was 17 and my daughter was 15, so we wanted to make sure we had a definite diagnosis. When the diagnosis came through it was obviously completely devastating. I think the hardest part of everything, including the treatment, was telling my kids. My daughter asked if I was going to die and would she get breast cancer. My son was very angry, he picked up his guitar and was just bashing away at it (which is typical of him actually!).

Within a couple of weeks, I had surgery (a lumpectomy), I also took part in a particular biopsy trial. This is where they inject an isotope into you, which travels to your lymph nodes under your armpit. If it has gone beyond the first node then there is a possibility that the cancer has spread. Fortunately for me it hadn't, and it was contained. After that I had six rounds of chemotherapy. I lost all my hair over summer, which was quite cool as I didn't have to shave my legs! The NHS gave me a wig that was like a country western singer, a kind of curly thing. It was hilarious. It only came out at family gatherings – I do actually have a picture of my dog wearing it too. I had 32 rounds of fractions, that was radiotherapy at St Thomas' in London, which was exhausting. It would have been so useful to have a badge or something saying 'I am going through treatment', as I would actually have to ask people on the train if I could have their seat.

I am on prevention drugs now – they said for five years but it has now actually moved up to 10. So as of 2020, next year, I will not be talking them anymore. This does give me quite a bit of anxiety. I am a very positive person. Especially now and rather annoyingly so, probably. I found it really useful while I was going through treatment to speak to people that were going through the same thing as me. It is not normal what you are going through, so you need support. You are in a bubble for nine months, of appointments and surgery and drugs. Yes, you can speak to your parents and your friends and your husband, but they don't really 'get it'. It's very hard to convey what's going on and, plus, you don't want to off load too much. In the end it gets boring talking about cancer, I am boring myself.

Saying that, I do think having that community around you is really important. People reach out in many different ways, but for me it was online. I didn't know these people I was talking to, but we shared tips about advice. It was through Macmillan, Cancer Research and Breast Cancer Care that I found a lot of support groups. For me I just wanted to find out more and more about my treatment and how I might feel physically. I do feel very fortunate to have been able to reach out and get that support.

At that time, I didn't know anyone else in my circle of life that was going through cancer. It was only until I had finished my treatment that my sister in law was diagnosed and her story is very different. She didn't want to talk about it. I guess that is okay, it is a personal thing. Not everyone wants to share, but for me I really needed it because it actually made me feel okay and that other people were going through it as well, so it was somewhat 'normal'.

Here I am now, nearly 10 years later. I am volunteering with a cancer charity and part of my job is talking to people on the street about their health and how they can help themselves. I just think it is so important to speak to people, because culturally a lot of people won't discuss breast screening or cervical cancer. People of my generation, in those communities especially, do not want to talk. It is shunned and frowned upon and it's a worry because there are probably quite a few people out there that are not receiving the help and support that they need. They find it very difficult and it is something that needs to be encouraged. My favourite experience was visiting a mosque in Whitechapel in London, we didn't know how we would be welcomed as it was about cancer, but we were received with open arms. We had so much interaction with the men and were shown around the women's part of the mosque and spoke to the women. Honestly, it was fantastic but there is still this stigma within a lot of communities.

I am so passionate about my volunteering job because if that lump was a little deeper and I had waited five years on for that screening I probably wouldn't be here talking to you. My cancer was quite aggressive – by the time I had the mammogram, to the time I got it removed two weeks later, it had actually grown quite substantially. I was elated to be free of cancer at that point. So yes, I want to give something back.

This is an edited transcript of an interview between Helena Traill and Alexandra on the 27th March 2019

Justin

090

I'm finished?

Background: I was diagnosed with a high-grade osteosarcoma, or aggressive bone cancer. There are 800-900 new cases of osteosarcoma each year in the United States and half of those cases are in children. I am a generation removed from childhood. Oh, and to remove the tumour located in my left scapula, my whole scapula was removed. I now have a new titanium shoulder and shoulder blade.

I'm finished? This is the title I am going with. I wrote it the day after I finished chemotherapy while still feeling all of the effects of the drug in my body. Chemotherapy was a grind. It was the most tiresome and physically difficult time in my life. While that is now behind me, I took a few weeks to write this and come to terms with my journey and what lies before me. Much of my life has changed. How do I describe to you the utter elation I feel, now that I have finished with chemotherapy? How do I describe to you the ever-present feeling that I may not ever be done with this? How do I describe living with the after-effects of my prosthetic shoulder and shoulder blade? I am not attempting to capture the emotions and feeling across my journey to this point. I want to understand where I am now. And I feel I am now at a crossroad.

Unless you've stared down a path of almost certain doom, it's hard to understand where I am now. Over the last 16 months, I endured 265 appointments. 265 appointments. 265 appointments from the time my shoulder first hurt through the end of treatment. It is hard to figure out what to write. The path has been long – and I don't feel like I'm done. I prefer to think in areas of black and white. I prefer a start, a middle, and an end. The end is important. Just as in any project – whether it's a household chore or work-related – I always strive to complete the project and celebrate the end. Celebrating the end is important. That is what is hard about where I am at. Sure, I am finished with chemotherapy. That is huge. A huge step in the right direction. But this was a journey I never wanted to take. And this 'final' step means I will carry the effects of this project with me for the rest of my life.

Upon diagnosis, I told myself to 'feel all the feels'. I knew I would not get through without emotionally understanding of where I was and what I needed. I wanted to pay attention to the little things because I knew there would be many difficult times. My priorities changed. I deliberately changed them. That's one way of putting it. If we look at life as a linear path from birth to death, for me, I see a beginning and an unknown end. Few of us contemplate what the end means to us. We instead talk about our journey along that path. The journey is what matters. Our stops along the path, where we take time to reflect on past experiences, the wide places on the path where we join up with friends and family at birthdays, weddings, funerals, should be meaningful. I deliberately focused on those meaningful times and tried to be present at as many as possible.

The middle part of my journey was easy. That was the part after my diagnosis and before my end of treatment. I had 16 one-week rounds of chemotherapy and surgery between the middle rounds. Easy. Well, easy emotionally. It was hard on my body with the side effects, stays in the hospital, and a constant feeling of being worn down. Still, I found that period the easiest to manage. When I said I wanted to 'feel all the feels', I also took the approach of surviving each day. There is a calmness to this approach. My laser-focus on surviving each day did not allow me to worry about the future or have despair about my past. I was not focused on my diagnosis. I was not focused on the changes to my body. I was focused on getting through each day.

There was a cadence to my treatment – one week on, two weeks off. My treatment weeks were simple. Monday – show up for labs, see my oncologist, then go to the infusion centre to receive pre-meds, chemotherapy, and be connected to a take-home pump that continuously infused another chemotherapy drug. On Tuesday, return with the pump, have more labs, pre-meds, a chemotherapy infusion, and refill the pump. I would repeat this process Wednesday, Thursday, and Friday, then return Saturday to be disconnected from the pump, receive a Neulasta shot and go on my way. I even worked in my shoulder rehab while I waited for my infusion. I was able to lose myself in my day-to-day effort to survive treatment. The cadence helped.

Now that cadence is over. My daily and weekly rituals ceased. What I think I am trying to write is that yes, I am super excited my treatment is done. I am super excited to move on from this constant feeling of weariness. However, now the repetition is gone. My future is unknown. I knew I needed to accomplish 16 rounds of chemotherapy to reach the end of treatment. I am now finished with the security of treatment and I have entered cancer survivorship.

What do I do with my free time? How do my priorities change? I feel lucky to ask these questions. Lucky that I have another opportunity to dramatically shift my priorities and focus on the things in my life that matter. I get to focus on my family and all the things that create joy in the world. I get to rebalance my life. I know my priorities will not shift back to their pre-diagnosis state, and I will never be the same physically or emotionally. For sure, my shoulder will always be different. But my hope is that my perspective, my outlook on life, has forever changed. In a way that I delight in small experiences. Merely writing the word 'outlook' conjures feelings and thoughts I have not spent much time on, during the last 16 months and I cannot describe how good that feels.

Here is to my transition. A transition from a laser-focus to one day at a time to a focus on letting my body heal, a focus on family, a focus on friends and a focus on the future. I don't know what the future holds – anyone who has had a cancer diagnosis knows this fact – but I do know I want to truly enjoy the life I have. And I am thankful I can enjoy my life with you.

091

I was diagnosed with Chronic Myeloid Leukaemia when I was 22 years old and studying at the University of Edinburgh. So Chronic Myeloid Leukaemia, or CML (because the NHS loves acronyms) is quite rare and unusual. I've got 'old mans' cancer because most CML patients are in their 60's or 70's and are male – generally speaking. So, I'm double-y rare because if you're aged between 16 and 24 when you're diagnosed with cancer then you're in a very special little cohort of teenage young adults (TYA) and anyone diagnosed when they're a TYA is rare regardless of what they're diagnosed with.

CML is a type of Leukaemia and there are 137 different types of blood cancer, CML is just one of them. I guess I'm lucky, depending on how you look at it. I will have it for life, so I take a pill of chemotherapy every day to manage it, and I have done for just over 12 and a half years. I have been on every available treatment to date. The names are ridiculous, I don't know where they get their names from. Even though my Leukaemia has always been very well managed, I have had an issue across all the other treatments because I am a sensitive responder. This current one is still only in trail, but I've got compassionate use because I can never tolerate standard dose.

So, the drugs work and I live in this medically managed place. If I were to come off treatment, then it would escalate. Before these pills were developed in 2000, your life expectancy was about five years for CML. So, this treatment discovery was a game changer. But I have lived with (not so much recently, but I'm keeping an eye on it) quite debilitating chronic fatigue as a side effect across all treatments. And until last summer I was very much considering a stem cell transplant for increased quality of life. Rather than for 'I'm going to die' reasons (which is why most people have it – when it's their only option to survive).

After I was first diagnosed, I was in my own room on a critical ward. I didn't realise how ill I was because I felt alright – I felt a little weird, but not that ill. I did not leave that room until I was discharged. So, it took me quite a long time to interact with anyone else who had cancer because when I was diagnosed, I had three questions – Will it kill me? Probably not. Can I still drink? Yes. Can I have children? Yes. That's all I needed to know. I didn't ask anything else which meant they didn't think I was taking anything on board because I wasn't asking anything else. Even still, that's all I've needed to know (even though I gave up drinking nearly 11 years ago, unbelievably).

I have experienced very poor care from consultants and my treatment is consultant lead. I'm very unusual as a cancer patient. I'm not normal. I haven't been through that process of intravenous chemotherapy, radiotherapy and surgery. Chronic cancers are managed in a very different way. So, I was diagnosed on 19th January 2007 and it took until October 2009 for me to interact with anyone else with cancer. I just wanted to surround myself with my healthy friends, I wasn't interested. 12 years ago, cancer was where mental health is now. People were talking about it, but it was still the 'C-word'. I think that's because The Press (and charities) talk about cancer in a way that doesn't necessarily reflect how lots of people feel. I thought everyone with cancer was bored, full of tubes and stuck in a chair – which is not the case, as I have discovered.

I went to a Teenage Cancer Trust conference called 'Find a Sense of Tumour' and tumour humour is what gets you through. You can say things, which to others sounds horrific, but you can say it. I have a friend who is in the army and before he went on his first tour, I said, 'Don't die in the lands of death' and he said, 'Well, don't let cancer kill you'. And people couldn't believe that (A) I had said that and (B) he had retaliated with that. But it's fine, you can do that. When I went to that conference, I saw people my age, with hair, smiling and having a good time – who had had cancer or did have cancer. That completely changed my attitude to wanting to be around others with cancer.

I think because I have very long gaps between hospital appointments, I haven't made many friends at my clinic. I am just an in-and-out person. When the leukaemia is stable, usually at three months or six months check-ups, the chance of you seeing other patients is slim-to-none and most people in my clinic are old. I don't really want to talk to them because we are in very different places. The one I did start to talk to was because I almost threw a cup of water over him. Classic. He was a few years older, maybe 38? On the other hand, I do know the staff well and I get on with the receptionist – it's a bit of a gang.

In terms of online cancer group and The Press, I don't like the language used, in fact I get quite angry about it. I'm not a survivor. I don't associate with that at all. I'm not fighting, I'm not winning, I'm not losing, I'm not battling. I'm just living and doing each day the best I can. But I have made some amazing friends and only know some from having cancer. It's about talking – I think, for the first time ever, I spotted someone on the tube with a Cancer On Board Badge and I said, 'Oh, hello, where did you get that from?' And they say, 'I got it through a charity' and I said, 'Oh, great, I'm one of the trustees'. We were having a chat and we were on the tube for a little bit. I said, 'So what was your diagnosis and how's your treatment been?' I was asking all these fairly personal and invasive questions, but it's okay because then they could ask me the same. Which is fine because you know there's no judgement, there's nothing like that. It's just we have got this in common – I know how you feel, you know how I feel and we can talk about it.

This is an edited transcript of an interview between Helena Traill and Katie on the 26th March 2019

James

092

Well, obviously, I had cancer. Tonsil cancer specifically which is, well, who gets tonsil cancer, it's so weird? I had chemotherapy first and then radiotherapy. Chemotherapy wasn't actually that bad considering I was expecting much worse. The particular drugs they gave me don't make your hair fall out, so you look quite normal. But it gave me nosebleeds and mouth ulcers. I felt mostly ok, most of the time, a bit tired – but ok. When I got to the end of my chemotherapy, I was given radiotherapy. Every day for six weeks. You can't miss a day because you don't feel like going. You have to go in and every day you become progressively more tired. Because it's in my throat, they said you're not going to be able to speak and you're not going to be able to swallow (I wasn't expecting that one). They put this horrible tube in my stomach, so they could put this weird milkshake through, it was all rather grim – but it was the fact that I couldn't speak that shocked me the most.

Gradually I went from whispery, whispery conversations to absolutely nothing. I had this weird (almost) silent conversation in the hospital one morning. It was a very hot day in August, and I stopped to talk to this chap who was/had basically the same as me. He had a bottle of morphine in his pocket that he kept swigging it, like some kind of wine'o on a bench. And we were saying, 'Oh, you know, what a terrible journey it was in today, really hot, and no one lets you sit down'. One of us said we should get some of those badges that pregnant women wear to see if it worked. It was just a bit of a joke. And the more I thought about it, the more I thought, yes why not. What's the worst that can happen?

I didn't actually do anything about it until I was quite a lot better, because I couldn't really concentrate on anything. So, when I was better, I found a website online where you can design your own badges. I made a hundred 'Cancer On Board' badges, based on the 'Baby On Board' Transport for London (TFL) badges (using the same font and logo). It was through Twitter that I started getting the badges out there, it caught on like wildfire. One of the first people who received a badge told me they knew these lawyers who would do the paperwork for nothing, so that it can become a charity. I met up with the lawyers and before I knew it, I was running a charity.

Eventually TFL got in touch with me and I thought right here we go. Here is the conversation where they say, 'You've had your fun but that's our trademark and you must stop'. But, actually, they were super nice about it. They told me I could use their logo as long as I was giving the badges away for free and not selling anything. But the trouble was, using their logo made it look like we were part of TFL and therefore geographically based only in London. I was worried people would think, 'Oh that's a London thing and it's just for the tube'. So, we decided to make our own logo. I had a friend of a friend who was a designer and she offered to help us. She started by giving us a few options and that's how we came up with our new badge. The new logo, which is used to create all the 100 Stories portraits, is all connected, one of the rings is going through and infiltrating the other rings – which is what cancer does. And at the same time, it is like a flower (many charities use flowers in their logos) and a snowflake, which I like.

Sometimes I still get quite tired, normally in the evenings, so actually wear my Cancer On Board badge quite a lot. More as advertising for the charity because people come up to me on the train and say, 'Where do I get one of those badges?' Or, 'What's that all about?' In response I give them a card explaining it. Recently someone on the tube asked, 'Have you got cancer?' I told him that I did, and he said, 'My brother has just been diagnosed with cancer and I don't know how to talk to him. I don't know how to start the conversation'. This makes me think I've become a sort of ambassador for cancer. But I don't mind talking about it, and if it helps that gentleman on the train talk to his brother, then it's a good thing.

During my diagnosis I turned to #CancerTwitter, which is a real thing by the way, and a great thing at that. There is so much support out there with loads of patients all taking part in daily conversations. If I am having a bad day, I will receive numerous supportive messages from them. I feel as though I know them all – even though I've never met them. They all say, 'Have you tried this?' Or 'Take your mind off it, do something else'. Included in this support network are some really good charities and organisations. If, for example, someone tweets, 'I've got breast cancer and I'm taking this drug and I have this side effect' someone will say, 'Oh!

You need to speak to this organisation because they have a 24-hour help line and you can ring them.' It's that instant response, putting people in touch with each other, which is revolutionary. Getting people talking to each other – that helps so much, in a way that I don't think any other platform can because social media (Twitter in particular) is so instantaneous.

What I have taken from all of this, is that you meet such wonderful people and you're in the 'gang' of being a cancer patient. It's the club no one wanted to join, but once you're in it, everyone is very friendly and there is a sense of coming together. It's like a community that you didn't know existed until you are part of it. The first thing you ask, or want to ask, when you're sitting in the waiting room and you see someone else is, 'Where's yours?' It's morbid but it seems to be acceptable behaviour amongst cancer patients. You often end up having very detailed discussions about your symptoms (the nasty side effects) and you learn to see the humour in it. That is really comforting and it's what gets you through it, at the end of the day. The support from friends and family, but especially from other patients, is invaluable, because when you realise someone is having a bad day, everyone rallies around and if you're not having a bad day, you do what you can for those who are.

This is an edited transcript of an interview between Helena Traill and James on the 26th March 2019

Georgina

093

I'm 26 years old, diagnosed at 26, still 26. So, if we start from when I got sick, I thought had the flu. I was off work for a couple of weeks and it was only when I came back to work that I found a lump on my neck. I used Google and self-diagnosed myself and went, 'Uh, damnit, I've got cancer.' Then I called up my doctor and said, 'Look, guys, I've got cancer and I need to get an appointment.' I even told my mum, 'Look, it's Hodgkin's Lymphoma, I know what it is.' The minute you go online there is a list of all the symptoms, and I could literally tick every one. So, I get to the doctor and am asked to state my symptoms so I said, 'I've got a lump in my neck, I've got flu like symptoms, I've lost a lot of weight in a short period of time (I thought my dieting was working really well), I'm getting night sweats and for about a year and half before the worst itching, like the most un-scratchable scratches all over my legs.'

I'd been to the doctors before about the scratching and they told me it was just eczema or hives, or it was stress. It turns out that was a symptom of Lymphoma. I was quite lucky, I quickly diagnosed. I had about two weeks of CT scans and biopsies and all the fun stuff. And then literally, I was called on a Thursday saying, 'You've got stage 4 Hodgkin's Lymphoma' and I was in chemotherapy on the Friday. So, within two weeks I'd gone from thinking I had glandular fever (let's be honest) to stage 4 cancer and going into chemotherapy. I had six months of ABVD chemotherapy (a combination treatment to treat Hodgkin's Lymphoma), which was every two weeks and that finished about six weeks ago.

Because I'd been told it was suspected Lymphoma, blood cancer, I didn't really talk about it until I got the official diagnosis and then I went straight into chemotherapy. So, I didn't discuss it until the next day and I was like, 'Right, everyone! This is what's going on. I don't want to be visited just yet. I need a bit of time to get my head around it.' Then once I had that week to feel like death, and I was in and out of hospital a little bit, I decided to use Instagram as my diary. I wanted to vocalise everything and anything. All for my own personal, selfish reasons, not for anyone else. With that, your friends start asking questions or people online start asking questions and I found it quite easy to be open.

When I lost my hair, that was a bit strange because you go outside, and people stare. It's still quite unusual to see a girl without any hair, but I would always prefer if someone comes up to me and says, 'Can I ask what's going on?' Or 'Is it cancer?' Then I would be very open and tell them exactly what it is. But I think it's when people don't ask me those questions, I wonder why they are looking – so, I'd always prefer if people were open, and I think I have been pretty open from the start. I mean, look at my Instagram, I think I've probably been far too open at times.

I found going through chemotherapy quite fun because you sit and speak to other patients going through it. Within two minutes we were talking about bowel habits, how many times we'd thrown up (and what consistency) and what disgusting side effects we had to deal with that day. You can't really do that with other people. I wouldn't call up friend and tell them it's been three days and nothing has happened! So, it was very easy to be open with other people with cancer.

I think, as my treatment went on, I found a bigger community of people. I was always open with my friends, but there's an element of feeling like you don't want to be moaning, because essentially that's all I had. All I was dealing with for six months was chemotherapy, cancer, hair loss, horrible side effects and weakness. If someone calls you up and asks how you are you can't just say you're having a great time relaxing – instead it was always negative. So, I always found it quite hard to pick up the phone because I had nothing fun to discuss.

I have always used Instagram, since getting sick, as my mind diary. To explain how I feel each day, putting it out there. I always thought to myself if one person reads that and thinks they feel the same or 'so this is when she lost her hair' or 'this is when she shaved it' then it's been worth it. Because that's exactly what I did. The first thing I did was read blogs, go on Instagram and try to find everything I could. So, my Instagram was used like that and then I wanted to keep my brain going, because I'd stopped working, so I started writing a blog. I thought it would be cathartic relief for myself and a bonus if anyone read it. It was a bit of a moan rather than anything informative but, again, if anyone gets any use out of it that's brilliant, because I think that's the biggest fear, if you get cancer, is that you feel quite alone, and you think you're the only person in the world going through it. None of my friends or immediate family, apart from when I was younger, had been through cancer. I hadn't seen it. I didn't know what happened. I'd never seen a woman losing her hair or using social media as a tool for open discussion. You can go on online and see what other people have done, especially young girls. In my case, that was so helpful. If I can add a bit to it, I will.

The people that I've connected with on Instagram over the last seven months, have been without a doubt, the best people I've ever met – ever. It's all people who either have the same thing as me or are going through something similar. For months I'd speak to these people online, and then I went to a few events with a charity called Trekstock and met all of them. Now I've met most of the people that I've talked to online, through these events. We've got a WhatsApp group and we go out for dinner and it's really nice to be able sit, and even not to talk about cancer – but just be with people who 'get it'. As much as you've got your best friend or your boyfriend who can sit with you and talk to you, they don't understand. They don't understand what it's like to lose your hair and eyebrows, have your body change so much, the pain or all the bad stuff. So, it's nice to just sit with a community of people who understand. And if one of you are quiet because you're a bit tired then no one says, 'Is there something wrong? Are you ok?' It's normal. It's just normal.

This is an edited transcript of an interview between Helena Traill and Georgina on the 2nd April 2019

Anna

094

I had a dodgy tummy for a while. It got increasingly worse. My brother, who is four years younger than me has Crohn's disease. At the time he was in and out of hospital, he couldn't eat, and he was losing loads of weight. He was classed as anorexic because of his body mass and was off food, being fed a liquid diet only. As a result, my diarrhoea and constipation issues seemed like nothing important. I didn't even feel that ill, so I just kept putting it off. Then I started not being able to eat anything and I began to think that I had Crohn's too.

I went to the doctor and he sent me to a specialist. I had a colonoscopy and I was worried; I really didn't want Crohn's. I had never even thought of cancer. When I came out of the colonoscopy, they told me straight away and I thought it was a bit weird because all these people suddenly arrived. The curtain was drawn, and everyone came in. My sister works at the hospital as a bowel specialist nurse and so they called her down too. It was a bit odd, so I thought I must have Crohn's and she had helped treat my brother at the hospital there. Immediately after they said, 'Anna, I'm really sorry but you have cancer and it's quite a big tumour. We are going to send you off immediately to have a CT scan.' I then got loads of tea and loads of biscuits and I felt better. The rest was quite a blur, as I was given quite a few of drugs from the colonoscopy. The next day I saw my surgeon who had given us the good news that it hadn't spread but the bad news was that it was big and that they would have to operate immediately. So, I had my operation on the Saturday.

It was a very big blur and then post op (during the few days getting better) was really hard because I hadn't processed it at all. I hadn't really thought about it and then suddenly I was in a lot of pain and having just had this major operation all I could do was just lie there and think horrible dark thoughts on morphine. Those were the really bad days, probably the worst days out of the whole thing. Shortly after I was allowed to go home, getting out of hospital and into my own bed made me feel a lot better. Plus, the kids were home and they kept me busy. It doesn't matter how sick you are, your child will always want breakfast. I think that stops you from wallowing and worrying.

I then had to wait two weeks to find out what exactly it was – luckily it was big and horrible but was lazy so hadn't really spread anywhere. There were no lymph nodes effected, but it was in my blood stream, something called extramural vascular invasion (EMVI). Bowel cancer spreads two ways, either through your lymph nodes or EMVI. I had to have chemotherapy for the EMVI and that happened for eight months. I had a choice: at hospital with an IV or at home with tablets. With small kids, I didn't want to go into hospital regularly because I was worried about getting sick and infections, so I chose it have it at home (which was amazing). Being summer (I started in April and finished in November) there weren't too many sickness bugs because everyone was out and about, so I remained relatively healthy. I took lots of anti-sickness tablets and ate Imodium like tic tac's – but I functioned. I slept every day – really embraced the siesta.

I got the all-clear scan in January last year. That was all about my active cancer part, but the rest of the time in remission I found a lot harder. Having cancer and being sick with cancer – it was quite an active thing. I felt as though something was going on and I was doing something but being in remission is much more of a mental strain. I always wondered if it would come back or if I would get sick again. But now I feel really happy and healthy, I don't want to go back to that dark place (the mental aspect was definitely harder than the physical).

My sister who is obviously a bowel cancer nurse said to look online at Bowel Cancer UK, because they are a good and active charity. I asked lots of questions and then saw that they had a forum. The CEO puts out names and introduces anyone new to the platform. It was really nice to hear from and chat to other people going through the same thing. I didn't realise that had existed before. It can also be sad as people have died since it all began, that just makes you realise how important early diagnosis is – so many people aren't diagnosed early and it is just such a waste.

It's been quite a nice journey, is some ways, to see the light in the darkness. A friend suggested to write down everything I was thinking and feeling (as I am quite a talkative and expressive person anyway) so that when the boys are older, and they ask you about it, you can show them. Because I may not remember, or

I may not want to talk about – so I started to write this blog, for the boys. My friends then kept asking me how things were going, and I just couldn't be bothered to repeat myself. I used to just post the link on Facebook, Instagram and Twitter and from that it got bigger and more and more people read it. I did that for a year and shut it down last year when I was put in to remission thinking I wouldn't need to write anymore but actually I've really missed it, because, as I said, being in remission has been a lot harder than I ever thought it would be.

I think the openness and conversations about cancer is changing. Conversations on this topic have always been negative, scary and dark. I didn't notice this so much before I had cancer. I realised this when my eight-year-old asked why there were so many cancer adverts. Who knew there were so many? They even have them on children's television channels. They are always so sad, and he would get upset because I would say that my cancer was ok, but the adverts say that it's not and that everyone is dying. I think more and more people are surviving cancer and more and more people are affected by it. No one will go through life without having or loving someone with cancer – unless we start talking it will remain scary.

That's why I had to prepare the boys by explaining that I had a big lump in my tummy and that when I got home, I wouldn't be able play and be jumped on. Oliver was fine, Sam was quite upset when I got home. He had never seen someone so ill before. When I was stronger, I started taking my kids to school again and the word spread so quickly that I had cancer. People start to look at you a certain way with 'cancer eyes', and they would just come up to you and hug you like they weren't going to see you again. Everyone was heartbroken and most looked at me as if I'd already died. It's fear, I guess, because it's not talked about and normalised. When you normalise something, people face up to it more, they understand the symptoms more and they go to the doctors and friends to talk about it more. It's a lot more proactive and positive.

This is an edited transcript of an interview between Helena Traill and Anna on the 6th March 2019

Samina

095

I was diagnosed with breast cancer at age 45 and it was the biggest bombshell I could ever be given. I had just completed a 16-year service in the local government, so had just applied for a new job which I was starting in September, and I was diagnosed in August. How did the diagnosis happen? Well, basically, my husband and I were together one evening and he said 'There's a lump' and I said, 'No, there isn't.' I'd never checked, and I don't know why I never checked. I think that was the other thing, I was so angry with myself because it wasn't on my radar. I never did monthly checks of my breasts or anything and it was him that said there was a pea feeling. But then I contacted the doctor to say that something wasn't quite right. We don't have any history of cancer in our family, at all. In other families and households, it may be quite common, but for us I was the first and it was a big shock.

I remember silly things, like ringing the doctor and then finding out that my doctor, who was female, wasn't going to be available for four days. Then I made an appointment with a male doctor, then I changed it and said, 'I'll just see who's available.' But then I thought it doesn't matter and I needed to know. Then I was referred, and this journey began.

I don't think I knew what to expect or what was going to happen. Everything happened very quickly, that was the other thing. It was a bit like a landslide – quickly, quickly – snowballed – and I was going from one appointment to the next. Maybe that was good because I didn't have time to think or overanalyse it. But I do remember falling to the ground, physically and emotionally. I remember, once they'd done the biopsy and I was sent home, I was told to have a week and not think about it. But it's impossible. You can do nothing but think, 'I've got cancer.' We had a family wedding and I remember my sister told me to get up and get ready. There were physically no changes, nothing had happened, but my heart and head couldn't get in that space. I wouldn't go anywhere, I felt like I'd just been thrown to the ground. I'd started my new job and then I went off after three weeks because I'd spoken to the manager. I was really lucky because the new manager was brilliant, she really supported me. But the whole diagnosis had just happened out of the blue and that's what shocked me.

I had stage 2 breast cancer. My one was hormone induced, so I knew that it was my hormones that were causing me the problem because that was the type of cancer I had. I also just thought that I would have surgery and be in and out. But that wasn't the case – things developed. After the biopsy, the tumour (kind of) exploded and I don't know if it was going to grow at that pace anyway, or was it because it got slightly tampered so it just grew? For me, it felt like everything had been ramped up a gear very quickly, but the doctor said that it would have happened anyway. I fell to the ground and I needed time to try and gather myself. I needed to grieve what I had just heard. I needed to get my head in the right space. I needed to understand how this was going to impact my family and my husband, my children, because it was this whole new space that I'd never experienced before. I knew it would be difficult and it was really difficult. I am a spiritual woman, I do believe in the universe, I do believe in God, and the minute I handed it to God and connected, I got some peace inside me. Then I got my head in the right space and told myself that I'll be alright: 'You are going to get through this.'

The social media part of my journey was really important for me. I took lots of pictures and I posted them on Facebook, which helped me. It was my way of coming to terms with it – by grieving and sharing with the world what was happening. Through that process I received a lot of messages from women to thank me for sharing. Many of the messages were along the lines of, 'My mother died from breast cancer, but we were never allowed to talk about it.' Or, 'My father forbids us from ever repeating that my mother had cancer.' I couldn't believe it, I can appreciate how hard it can be for the whole family, but suppressing what it is that you are going through makes it a lot harder. I felt God had sent me an army of people – I had some amazing friends on Facebook and they all connected. People that I knew from my childhood connected with me and they gave me great strength. Now, what you sometimes find in a cancer journey (and it isn't for everyone) is that some people, who are the closest to the patient, actually can't connect with them. They just can't. This could be because they are too close, they are in denial or they just find it really difficult. My siblings (especially my sister) found it really difficult. Obviously, her compassion, her love was there for me, but I think she was dealing with the grief of what's happening.

I think that sometimes you find and connect with different people and you get that army of people that carries you through. For me, social media was a good outlet. It was a good way of enabling me to say how I felt. Many evenings I couldn't sleep at night, I had insomnia and could upload pictures, talk about my day, say how I was feeling and where I was going. Just checking in. It felt like I was taking the world with me and I wasn't alone, and I think that was important – that you're not alone. I don't use Twitter, but I do use Facebook and LinkedIn because I feel like you can tell your story – people can give you well wishes and comments, but no one can judge you. You can tell your story as it is and that's what I love. I can voice my opinion and I'm not going to get shot down.

I also attended the Haven and lots of other groups for woman with breast cancer. I guess I was alone because I was the only Asian woman there. Some people even said to me, 'Oh, I didn't think that cancer affected Asian woman.' I realised I hadn't appreciated how much in the South-Asian community that cancer is a taboo. No one wants to talk about it – they don't want to say the C-word. People would come to visit me and say, 'Oh, she's ill'. They wouldn't say the word cancer. I had to sit there and tell them it's fine that I've got cancer, but I will get through it.

There were complications. I had a blood clot and ended up having to get the chemotherapy into me a different way. But that would have happened anyway, if it was leukaemia or any other major disease or illness. You're always going to get side effects.

In chemotherapy, one of the nurses said to me, 'You're one of a kind' and I would always laugh and tell her she could say that again. There were other Asian women that would come in with their head scarves on and they'd do their treatment, then wrap themselves up quickly and leave just as fast. It's as if to say that it wasn't really happening. I found that quite difficult because I'm not the same person I was before cancer and through the chemotherapy journey I changed as a person, the world around me changed as well. I think you have to give yourself back permission, time and acknowledgement. Because if you don't, then what you did before cancer (my hectic lifestyle, not having a great diet and trying to do everything) contributed to me becoming unwell. I'd compromised on my immune system and looking back; I don't want that lifestyle anymore. I don't want the seven in the morning to ten at night, running around. Now I can manage me better. I know now. I often say to people that cancer was 'good for me.' Which, I know, is a very bizarre statement, but it was good for me. I've met amazing people. I thought I was young in the chemotherapy unit but there were so many young people. Everyone's cancer is different and that's what we have to remember. It's all different.

This is an edited transcript of an interview between Helena Traill and Samina on the 25th March 2019

lyna

096

When I was diagnosed, I was 30 years old. My son was only five, I had just got a new job, just moved to a new house a month before, and my son had started private schooling in September. I was diagnosed three months later in January. So literally, within three months I had gotten a new job, son started school and we'd just bought a new place, so it was quite big. It was quite exciting times, to be fair, because we could see our family and our new life, even me personally (with my career) it was all going upwards. It was incredible.

Then I was diagnosed with stage 3 breast cancer and all I can recall is the surgeon saying, 'I'm really sorry but you've got stage 3 breast cancer. The tumours are the size of a golf ball and we're going to have to operate. Please write off the next 12 months. You will lose your hair and there's not going to be much that you're able to do.' To be fair to them, I think they have to give this news to so many people, so many times in a day, that they have to detach themselves from it, from the emotions of it all – it was quite cold.

There was a lot of information in the first meeting and I dealt with it in a way that reflects how my parents brought me up. Growing up if we had the flu, we weren't allowed to mope around in the living room, on the sofa. My dad's attitude was to go and get paracetamol, get up and don't lie around downstairs, 'Don't sit here and moan and groan about it. Come on. Get up. You'll be fine, you'll be fine. Get up and go.' It was that sort of thing. It was just 'man up' and 'you'll be fine'. He was like that with his sons, he was like that with his daughters, he was like that with all of us. So, I've very much grown up with that, and I'm very much like that in my personal life. So, when cancer came it was no different.

For me I didn't think about being upset or sad, I just asked what I needed to do next or what does that mean? Those were my exact words to the surgeon: 'What do I do next?' He looked at me and told me my treatment plan, I didn't cry, and I didn't get upset. I went into fight mode and decided I just needed to get through it.

I put my head down. Very tunnel vision and I didn't want to look left, look right, or do anything else. I came off social media because I didn't want anyone to see me looking like I'm ill. It's strange really because I'm so different now, I don't stop talking about it. Whereas when I was going through it, I was completely different. I didn't want to talk about it. People used to say to me, 'Why don't you go to these groups and speak to people who've also got cancer, so you understand, and they understand you?' But I decided I didn't want to remember or talk about cancer. Why would I want to be around people who have got cancer, and talk about it even more? I didn't want to be around people who've got cancer. I didn't want to be around people going through the same thing as me. I just want to get my head down and get to the other end and forget it even happened. So that's why I came off social media. I didn't talk to anybody. I don't think I even had my phone most of the time because I knew people would call and see how I was and check in and I didn't want to see those messages – people asking how I was all the time. It just felt like sympathy and I hated that. I didn't want people to feel sorry for me. I can fight it. I can do it. I don't need someone to ask me if I'm okay, stop asking me that! I was always consoling people more than they were consoling me.

But I did struggle. I struggled very much. I struggled with the things I felt were out of my control, if that makes sense. I coped as well as I could, physically with the pain. Chemotherapy is horrid. I don't even think horrid is the right word. It really is the worst thing anyone could ever go through, and if there's anything worse, somebody please tell me what it is. There's nothing to explain just how awful it is and for a woman with breast cancer, it's the worst thing any woman could possibly imagine. Anything that you feel makes you feel feminine is gone. You lose your hair, you lose your breasts, you lose your eyebrows, you lose you eyelashes. You look pale and you gain two stone worth of weight. Sex is no longer an option. You completely lose all those emotions and feelings. Anything that you associate, generally, with a woman… you lose. It's horrid, it really is.

A mother's instinct is to care for your kids, care for your family, and you don't even have the energy to even do that. My five-year-old son would want me to get him dressed for school, but I physically couldn't get up to help him. I couldn't close the buttons on his shirt because I didn't have the energy to do it and watching someone else have to do that for me was heart-breaking – I've always done that for him. I've always worked full time, but I've always worked that time around doing things for him, dropping him to school and then going to work and doing my things. It's changed my whole life. I could manage the pain and take some form of pain killers and sleep. I could lie down and tell myself that the pain will go away and I'll be fine, I'll be fine – it's another week and a half and then I'll have a good week and then I'm back to chemotherapy, then I'll have another good week and I'll be back.

What I couldn't deal with, emotionally, was the way I looked. Some people, family and friends around me, struggled with that too. They struggled because I was struggling. They couldn't understand why I struggled so much with the way I looked because people would always say that at least I was alive. But I would look in the mirror and would see that I'm not who I've always been. Overnight, somebody has taken away something from me and I had no choice about it. I struggled with that. I struggled with the fact that when I walked out that front door, although I could hide the pain, because that was in my control, I couldn't control that I had lost all of my hair. I couldn't control that I looked like a cancer patient. I couldn't control that I had no eyebrows and eyelashes and I was three stone heavier, than ever in my life. One thing that sticks in my head, throughout my 11 months of my treatment, the only thing that I really remember and stands out, and the only thing that gets me down is remembering the day I lost my hair.

I remember going into the shower with a full set of hair, it was all crumpled together like it had been burned, but it was my full set of hair. I refused to go into the shower for five days because I knew what was going to happen if I put water on my hair. I went in for the shower at my parent's house, because I couldn't be on my own, so I was living there, and I put water on my hair and literally chunks just fell down. I came out of the shower with two strands of hair, literally two strands, and I had gone in with a full head. I'm not hugely religious, I'm not hugely spiritual to be honest with you, but in that moment all I can remember is screaming and shouting, 'Allah, Allah, give me strength. Give me strength. Please give me strength. Please give me strength.' I was screaming and I remember my parents standing outside the door, banging the door, saying, 'We don't care if you have no clothes on, please just open the door and let us come inside. Please let us come inside.' Because they were helpless, they didn't know what else they could do other than shout for them to come and hug me. Even my dad was standing there and he's quite religious, he prays five times a day and always has done, my mum is the same. So, for my dad to turn around and say, 'I don't care if you've got no clothes on, I don't care what the situation is, please just open the door' that is massive. That's huge because for him he just wanted to show support.

I struggled – I didn't leave the house much. I wouldn't let anyone take pictures of me. I remember going to my brother's house and they were all taking pictures because everybody was dressed up and I asked for no one to take pictures of me. I was really serious, and I got really annoyed because one of our family friends was sent a picture by my sister and they put it on social media. I was really angry because I didn't want anybody to see me.

But I came out the other end after struggling for a year, being on antidepressants with insomnia. And then I realised, when I did go back onto Facebook, so many people had sent me messages to say nice things. I started to then talk about my journey, about a year and a bit after, because I felt I was in a better head space at that time. Then I started to talk about how cancer can affect somebody and how it can affect you in different ways and how in the South-Asian culture I heard so many odd things. Things like if you wear a black Hijab, then the cancer will go away. Or people telling me to pray and the cancer will go. Even, 'Don't be silly, don't have chemotherapy or any treatments.' It was just 'don't do this' and 'don't do that.' I heard someone say that I just needed to have faith and that I must have done something wrong in life because this was God's punishment to me. 'So, what have you done wrong? Think about what you've done wrong. Go further toward religion, that's why you're in the situation that you're in.' All of those sorts of things and I always thought, in my head at the time, what did I do wrong? Did I do something, like they said? Was I working too hard? Was I working too much? Was I weakening my immune system? What have I done wrong in order for me to be in the situation that I'm in? So, I started to share those things on Facebook and a lot of people got in contact.

This is an edited transcript of an interview between Helena Traill and Iyna on the 25th March 2019

Ann-Marie

097

My name is Ann-Marie and I am the director of a charity that aims to end female genital mutilation called 28 too many, and I've been doing the work since 2005. My original career background was in human resources and professional corporate life, I ran my own business and then set up a charity and worked in Africa. My life was ticking along well; I'd achieved what I wanted to do in life, and I'd managed to get a degree or two. I got a doctorate, a sports car and my own property to live in. All the things one associates with a successful life.

When suddenly I had just been out to Africa a week before, when I noticed a tiny little pea shaped bump in my hip socket (in my groin). I didn't really think much of it. I thought it was probably a lymph node, it was sort of the thing you'd get if you had a cold (if you got a sore throat or something). I had one in my neck that I'd had for a few years that had been investigated and they said it wasn't anything suspicious, so I thought it was another one like that. But then I went to Africa, I probably spent about a minimum of four months abroad each year, came back and that weekend I looked in the mirror and it looked much bigger. It looked like a lozenge, about maybe an inch long and slightly rounded. It filled that socket on the one side of my body and I thought 'that's a bit strange'. I got back from Africa on the Sunday and on Tuesday I got a day off because my friend was coming to London and she cancelled because she had to relocate for work to somewhere else. I thought, 'Well, I'll go to the doctor and just have it checked out'. I had something else too, some aches and pains in my jawline and thought, 'Oh, I'll ask about that'.

At the end of the appointment I said to the doctor, 'Oh, there is one other thing', and she said, 'There can't be one other thing, we only had time for one thing per appointment'. Which is actually a bit brutal and I think it's lucky it was me or I think I would have left and not bothered. It's quite sociologically hard to go to the doctor about something you're worried about (although I wasn't that worried), and then pursue it, if the doctor is running out of time. The first thing she said was 'this is serious', which is a really weird thing to say and I just remember thinking what the heck does that mean. Then she got out her little ruler and measured it. She turned her head to the computer and typed and typed. She then said, 'I don't think the physiotherapy referral I've just made for you is going to sort out your aches and pains.'

I didn't really understand what I'd been through or what had happened. I didn't know what to look up and I didn't feel unwell. About five days later a letter came through the post. I was going up to the Lake District to see my cousins, and it had pinged through the door. So, I took the letter with me because I didn't think I could make the appointment and it was a letter from haematology. 'Heama' being blood and 'tology' being cancer. Well, that definitely was serious, but I didn't feel unwell so I didn't think it could be and I didn't know what it could be anyway. When I returned, I went to my oncology meeting and they wanted to do more tests.

I had the tests done, I negotiated with a consulted because I was going out to Sierra Leone to do my work for three weeks. There was a week coming up, then he was away for a week, then I was away for a week. So, I said, 'If I had the tests all done the following week then I could go out to Africa.' I'd agreed to come in for the results the day after I came back from my holiday. He was very clever, the way he shared the news. He said, 'I think what we might be dealing with what is called a lymphoma.' But I didn't know what that was anyway and I thought it could be either benign or malignant. I kind of remembered Googling 'lump in groin' but you get all sorts of things like 'a pulled muscular muscle strain'. I didn't particularly worry and then when I came to the results, he told me he was right, and it was lymphoma.

He was very clever because he never used the 'cancer' word. We talked about it because I'd been booked to go to Cuba on holiday, but it looked like Cuba was going to be a sacrifice. He was worried about the health care there, amongst other things, but actually within about three weeks I was fairly ill. I'd got about 11 lumps and bumps come up all over, top to bottom of my body and torso. I'd got an infection, so the day I was due to go into the hospital, maybe three weeks after the diagnosis, I was too ill to have the chemotherapy. I ended up about five days in hospital. They tried to get rid of the infection before I could have the chemotherapy. That was the beginning of my cancer journey, and then what followed was 24 cycles of chemotherapy and immunotherapy. I had the first lot of doses, two every three weeks from July till December and one dose every eight weeks for the following two years. So that was two and a half years, with one infection that slowed it down for a month or so (that was when my blood went too low and I went to neutropenic and couldn't have any chemotherapy for a while). Apart from that, I did quite well and now it's been about a year since I've finished treatment, for now. I'm waiting for what will happen next. It is expected to grow back. It's just a case of what and when, so I'm trying to balance how to do my life.

Both my parents had terminal cancer, they didn't get to their retirement, so I'm determined to have my retirement. The challenge for me is to fulfil the things I want, the dreams and wishes while I have the time and energy, and health. With the expectation that I might not get the classic retirement. So that means doing everything I want to do in the present, as well as everything I need to do from the past and need to do in the future. All in the same window of time, with my symptoms and side effects of chemotherapy, which is quite challenging. That's where I'm up to.

I've got a faith, so for me having that faith meant I could write out to maybe 20 people who also had faith. In the beginning for those three weeks when I went out to Africa, I wrote to a bunch of people who were key friends. They happened to be Christians or from key Churches who were also involved with the female genital mutilation work I do. I said, 'I'm writing to you because I've had some serious concerns from my doctor about my health and I'm going out to Africa but please pray that these tests don't show anything.' I think most people thought they wouldn't actually, but when they did then I started a dozen or so newsletters just saying points for prayer. I think that was one way told everyone and spoke about it. Many of my friends aren't very 'tech-y' so I didn't do it on anything else, but then I replaced that later on with a WhatsApp group and that carried on until I finished chemotherapy last March.

Some people were fine with it, some were not. People do say very random things. One person said, 'Oh, but you're the executive of our will. What's going to happen if you die first?', which isn't the most useful thing to say. Another lady who's maybe 20 years older than me, said, 'Oh, so it looks like you're going to be with our Jesus before me now then.' And again, that's not very helpful. People do say some really silly things. Other people try and give too much advice, tell you what to do. 'You should do this etc. I'm happy to be your executer' and 'How do you know it's that?' or 'How do you know how bad it is' or 'Surely, you can get better'. They had lots of views on things like that.

My cousin didn't really want me to tell my uncle because he's got health issues himself, a chronic condition, but she thought she'd have to tell him if I lost my hair – but then I didn't lose my hair, my hair thinned. That deprived me from a relationship with my uncle for two and a half years because I couldn't get to see him in Birmingham. So, who's the patient here? Who's the one to be cared for? I think that's a common part, I find. And then there's the whole other piece about protecting other people's feelings. That's a big part. I try and protect others whereas, actually, they should be protecting me.

My father didn't acknowledge that he had cancer. I don't think he knew when he died. I could be wrong, but I think my Mum chose not to have him know. My Mum did know she had cancer, but it went quite quickly from breast to brain, and my Dad's was in his liver. By the time it went to secondary, it was too advanced to have much conversation. A week of surgery, a week of not being able to talk and then a week of dying. I wanted to do it differently.

In the end, I kept off social media entirely for the early stages, in terms of sharing about cancer, but I did share what I was doing, and I had created 10 legacy plans which was quite nice to do. It gave me some element of choice in what I was doing – finishing things off, having time with my god-children, friends and family, being kind to myself and doing things that were relaxing and healthy. I did some work in a hospital, training as a Nun, and making a Bucket List as well. I knew that as soon as the intense chemotherapy stopped (it kept me house bound to avoid infection because of my immune system) I would start the Bucket List. The list began with about 25 items and grew to about 50 and then eventually, now, it's come to about 85. I've just completed number 39.

It's one a month and I've done it since January of 2016. There's no particular logic really. This year's list items were Bletchley Park in January, Paris in February to see the Moulin Rouge. Madrid was 10 days ago. Japan in April to see the cherry blossoms, but I might not be well next April, so I thought, let's seize the day. May is for Switzerland to see the Hadron Collider. Sometime between July and August will be the war graves in France and Belgium. Quite a lot were in London and the United Kingdom, so I did those first because they were easy. The very first was up the road doing a ballroom dancing lesson. Those give me joy and time with people, plus people seem to love doing those with me.

I'm on chapter four of the book I'm writing. It's about the charity's life and the 20 years of running it. I've enjoyed journaling daily since I was diagnosed, however the book is a legacy piece. It's my story, so when I can't get around the country to do talks or get around the world, which I used to do, it's there anyway. It's there to help people to think that it's not hard to do what I'm doing, and anyone can do anything if they put their mind to it.

This is an edited transcript of an interview between Helena Traill and Ann-Marie on the 29th March 2019

098

Diagnosed on the 25th of May 2015, at The James Cook University Hospital in Middlesbrough, with a type 3, high grade and type 2A low grade Non-Hodgkin's Lymphoma. The latter came with caveat 'incurable'. My lump was ignored for three to five years (I can't even remember how long I avoided them). Please, please don't be an idiot like me. Go get yourself checked out.

Treatment: Following Ultrasound, CT and MRI scans and a couple of fine needle biopsies, immediate surgery took place to remove the type 3 high-grade tumour cluster around my right scapula at The Friarage (The James Cook University Hospital). This was 100% successful – the high grade is no more! There then followed a course of radiotherapy in autumn 2016 at The Christie, Manchester, which destroyed the large type 2A low grade tumour cluster in my left groin. This removed the very large tumour but did not relieve me of low-grade Non-Hodgkin's Lymphoma (low grade simply refers to the rate of tumour growth).

Post-treatment: 'Watch & Wait' from December 2016, with monthly and then after eighteen months, quarterly visits to The Christie Hospital, Manchester. This continued until July 2019, when a more patient-focused 'Active Monitoring' was initiated at my new Haematologist at The Royal Berkshire Hospital following another whole-body CT scan.

The fiercest daily wrestling match I face, from the moment I open my eyes to staring, often weary beyond words, at the bedroom ceiling, is the unpredictable fluctuation in energy levels. Let's name it… chronic fatigue – that insidious curse of all cancer patients. Additionally, the frequent fluctuations between stable health, illness, and remission often boarders on the overwhelming. So many of us now live, or will live, under the lengthening shadow of incurable cancer, but have yet to reach the final stage of life. It is imperative that an open discussion around the reality of cancer begins, however difficult it may be. This project, 100 Stories, may well play a crucial role in this. It is my hope that it catalyses an ongoing debate.

Having lost control of all aspects of my own life since diagnosis and having experienced the amazing treatment and care under the NHS, I needed to do something, anything, even if illusionary, to say 'I am the master of my fate, I am the captain of my soul' (a line from William Earnest Henley's poem Invictus), I understood completely and almost immediately that my particular cancer was incurable. This, most unexpectedly, led me to immerse myself in an oasis of calm. Still, me being me, I needed to thumb my nose, cock-a-snook if you will and – you may find this odd and even shocking – even laugh at the absurdity of my situation. What else is there for me to do?

As a physicist, well, a teacher of physics at least, I decided to take a somewhat positivist and scientific approach to this experiment of self-development. Several assumptions were drawn up and defined. Questions were formed: What did I think the life I now had would be able to accommodate? What did I have to accept, however reluctantly, about my new reality? What did I actually have the means and opportunity to accomplish? What could I still do, and what could I no longer do? What, in essence, would add quality to my days and minimise the effects of the insidious monstrosity lurking within my lymphatic system?

Firstly, I read voraciously; it was and is almost an escape, from medical and scientific journals to popular science magazines, to podcasts and online courses. What transpired was rather unexpected and, in hindsight, somewhat simple. That which I just knew I couldn't hope to begin or maintain, or which smacked of pseudo-science (there is so much of this nonsense around – its disingenuous at best, and dangerous at worst. Stop preying on desperate people!) I discarded and then decided upon a simple plan. The following 'top 10 + 1 list' is my very much an anecdotal stream of consciousness.

I hope you, dear reader, may find something here that helps:

1. To walk daily. As I was now living in the family home caring for a terminally ill mother, I decided a canine companion would be a wonderful addition. So, meet Dexter the 40kg lurcher-greyhound cross. A weekend visitor from Northern Greyhound Rescue, who became a much-loved companion and friend. Our twice daily walks through Haigh Woodland Park are where my path to 'active monitoring' began to clear. He is missed, every day.

2. To volunteer. I wasn't able to teach in a laboratory for almost eighteen-months (goodbye savings) so the weekly park-run volunteering, with the wonderful and patient Haigh Woodland team, was a superb way to feel useful. To help such an amazing concept succeed and make a lot of new friends at a low moment was a real panacea. I also volunteered with the superb charity Lymphoma Action – their helpline was my initial lifeline. I remember pouring out my anger, frustration, fears, rambling questions, everything, while sat on a park bench the day after my initial diagnosis. I often wonder what passers-by thought of this deranged, weeping, ranting mad man?

3. To strength train as much as I could (which wasn't a great deal to be honest). I decided to invest my rapidly diminishing savings in a personal trainer to help me develop as much strength and power as possible. What actually happened was that I managed a single weekly session of very heavy, technique focused, compound lifting ending with a brutal 'finisher' (a HIIT of real magnitude). It usually took me between four to six days to fully recover. This was incredibly uncomfortable at times and the recovery was often horrid, however the cumulative effect of a little increased lean muscle and the psychological vigour gained for completing a session, I would have thought impossible, has proven to be a real boon to both body and soul. The hardest part was accepting that my recovery was not 'normal'. It took a while, but I eventually came to terms with this reality. Here's my rather dodgy hypothesis: greater muscle mass means an increase in mitochondria density, which means more effective energy regulation (with sincere apologises to the physiologists out there). Huge thanks to PT Helen Clewer of Box Bell Fit. I could not have done this without you.

4. To work to pay the bills. A return to teaching (part time). After a false start where things went completely pear-shaped, I now find myself in a wonderfully supportive school and have just increased my contact time from 60% to 70%. Again, it was not all smooth sailing, I was originally thinking I could manage 80% this academic year, however reality re-dawned and we quickly and smoothly dropped to 70%, which will be my ceiling. Thank you to all at Altwood CoE School, Maidenhead, for accommodating this highly irritating transition – you have been truly outstanding in your support. Additionally, the annual residential Deutsche Junior science academy near Münster, Germany, is my highlight. Meeting

the same leaders every year (2019 was our 11th year) and the wonderful students is pleasure beyond words. I always learn something new – this year it was the bongos!

5. To accept that my day is no longer 24 hours. What do I mean by this? I now work on an 18-hour day basis. I accept that there is a very high probability that I will lose a quarter of the time available through the need to rest – which is often a somewhat inglorious staring into space feeling rather 'hung over' or on the crux of a common cold, is the best description I can come up with of the ever present fatigue. This feeling, to a greater or lesser degree, is ever present. It is my sword of Damocles. But we are mighty and will not bend.

6. To ride my beloved bicycles. Despite taking part in Prostate Cancer UK's Grand Depart Classique, where a few hundred lunatics cycled 190 km (actually 220 km after a few unplanned detours. Average speed 19 km/h, so 10 hours of pootling around Flanders), following the 2019 Tour de France stage 1 course – on the hottest day recorded in European history – I have managed very little, no, I have managed zero cycling. See point 5. This is a bitter pill that I am reluctant to swallow. Plans are currently in the offing to see what can be done. An indoor trainer has been purchased from a stout and true friend. I just now need to re-start the riding.

7. I learned to accept that I deal badly with conflict of any kind, which leaves me utterly exhausted. It has taken a long time but I'm developing strategies to deal with this. It is not easy. A vast majority of people understand this however, such is the human condition, one or two have really tried to take advantage of me. They know who they are, and they know they no longer play no part in my life journey.

8. To finish every morning and post-gym shower with at least three-to-five minutes of cold-as-possible watery 'fun'. Yes, a cold shower. This seems to really kick-start the day. It's horrid to begin with but you soon adapt. Go on, give it ago.

9. Plant based eating. I endeavour to ensure my weekly diet is at least 80-90% plant based. Don't beat yourself up if you don't manage this but I really do feel the old adage 'you are what you eat' rings true. I also accepted the advice not to eat processed food, so, if it comes in a packet, I don't buy it. I'm incredibly fortunate in that I own a Thermomix which has transformed my home cooking, such that it is.

10. Friends. So much has happened to me. So many friends have helped. A huge amount. Be it a simple message via social media, an unexpected visit with pie and chips (yes, I remember Michelle and Nicola), a loan of money to get me through the dark days of home loss and inability to work, or the simple companionship of chat over a cup of tea. Often having bumbled no more than ten miles on the trusty steel steed. It is so important. Rich and Rory, you were genuine life savers. Nadja, you are my inspiration and all the motivation I need to keep forging ahead on this new path, less travelled.

10 + 1. Last, but by no means least – psycho-oncology. The ten tips listed above would have proved to be elusive indeed, if it was not for the transitional guidance of Anne Crook and her psycho-oncology team. It's a form of cognitive behaviour therapy tailored specifically to the needs of post-treatment cancer patients. Psycho-oncology provided the means to stoically hack my way onto and along the path less trodden between my former life and current reality.

For me, following a process is a far more powerful approach than aiming for an outcome. I've tried to develop an evidence-based outlook of genuine gratitude. It has changed my life for the better. The adventure still continues, as it does for us all. I live in very interesting times with so many ups and downs. At the time of writing I have another lump to investigate, this time in my jaw. Another biopsy is just around the corner. Whatever the outcome, we will persevere. We will endure. We will embrace the wonder that every single day brings.

Thank you for reading my anecdotal tales, and good luck to you. I may no longer be the master of my fate, but so what – the real strength lies in never giving up. As my true friend and soulmate often tells me, 'The sun always shines after a storm, sometimes you just have to force yourself to look for it.'

Vix

099

This is my story. I am on my third cancer in three years and still hell bent on continuing to do cancer at a canter.

In 2016 I was diagnosed with melanoma (skin cancer). It was just a mole on my calf, and it had been there for a couple of years. My doctor said it was perfectly round, perfectly flat and there was nothing to worry about. After about 12 months I was referred to a dermatologist. The dermatologist decided to remove the mole on my calf and another from my back. I was called back two weeks later and walked into a room to be greeted by three Macmillan cancer nurses all sat behind a desk. They told me it was bad news and that the mole on my leg was a melanoma. They explained they needed to take some more flesh from my leg to ensure wider (clearer) margins from around it.

So that was the start. That was my first real experience of any kind of cancer, I hadn't really thought about it very much before then. My mother had breast cancer when I was younger, but that was successfully treated. My grandfather died from skin cancer. My granny died from stomach cancer, my aunt died earlier this year from ovarian cancer and my dad very sadly died, incredibly suddenly from pancreatic cancer in 2016. Pancreatic cancer sits in the same family as bowel cancer.

In 2017 I had a tooth infection – it was a failed root canal that had been done two years earlier. My dentist gave me a very strong antibiotic called metronidazole and said that should sort it. It didn't. On the way home from a dinner party one evening, I knew I needed the loo fairly urgently. I ran up the steps to my front door but – there's no nice way of saying this – I shat myself. It was awful. After cleaning myself up I put it down to the metronidazole from the tooth infection (because that particular antibiotic is known for striping out all the good bacteria in the gut). Even the doctor told me it was probably from the metronidazole, but to be on the safe side, he referred me to a gastroenterologist. In fact, his exact words were, 'This is very unlikely to be bowel cancer, more likely IBS or something, but just to be on the safe side I'm going to refer you'.

My new doctor, Dr Poulou (very apt name), had the results of the bloods and said, 'You know what, if this was bowel cancer I'd expect to see this marker at this level, but it all looks perfectly normal. However just to be sure, we'll send you for a colonoscopy'.

The day I went into hospital for the colonoscopy, I was first on the list. I remember waking up and watching everybody in the recovery room being discharged and allowed home. This annoyed me intensely because I pack a lot into a day with my dogs to look after and riding my horse. All anybody kept saying was I had to wait to be discharged by Angie. But everybody else was being discharged by a myriad of different nurses. I couldn't understand why I needed to wait for Angie. Who on earth was Angie? What did Angie do? I clocked the girl on reception and asked her what Angie's job title was? 'Ah sure' she replied, 'I believe you're waiting to see Angie, she's one of the colorectal specialist cancer nurses'. Angie appeared moments later and took us into another room. I don't remember much about that conversation. I just remember Angie explaining that they had found a 10-centimetre tumour in my bowel.

Little did I know then that Angie was going to be a fairly major part of my life for the next three years. Angie and Amy are my specialist colorectal nurses. They are the nicest human beings and do an amazing job. They are there at the end of a phone number when you're being paranoid that you're neutropenic, you're scared, or you don't want to call the emergency chemotherapy hotline. They are there at all my oncology appointments, whatever the news and whatever the weather. They've shuffled me in the direction of counselling when they've recognised, I wasn't dealing with detaching from my work life very well, they've listened and sympathised when my long-term boyfriend ran off with someone else two weeks after my diagnosis. They may be dressed as nurses but to me they are complete angels.

It was a bit of a whirlwind following the results of the colonoscopy, I was in the middle of launching a new office, and they said they wanted me in for surgery three days later. This was going to be the first time I realised that unfortunately cancer takes priority over everything, hospitals become your life, literally everything else has to stop.

I felt I was on some kind of hideous rollercoaster that I couldn't get off and I no longer had any control over what was happening. I was told the bowel resection was going to be keyhole surgery. But afterwards I woke up to find a fairly large and gnarly wound, made worse by the fact that it had been glued rather than stitched. Of course, clearly a 10cm tumour was not coming out through a keyhole. But when you're new to all this, you just don't know. They also took 33 lymph-nodes, whilst they'd been there apparently. I think 33 lymph nodes is quite a lot to take (gauging other people's experiences), but my oncologist later said that none of them showed disease, however there were signs of disease in the blood vessels that supplied these lymph nodes. Turns out it was quite an aggressive tumour, my oncologist said she didn't like the way it had behaved. I didn't really care because they'd taken it out.

I just cracked on, the recovery was slow, I couldn't walk properly. I couldn't even lift a dog bowl. A few months later they started me on oral chemotherapy. They referred to it as a 'mop up chemo'. It was fine. I basically regressed into being a three-year-old child and couldn't be trusted not to poo myself quite a lot of time. You kind of get used to that! All in all, I took eight cycles of capecitabine, or did I have more? I can't remember ('chemo brain' strikes again). I was taking 28 pills a day, every day for two weeks, followed by one weeks break and then the cycle began again.

I wanted to go back to work during the chemotherapy, but I was worried about commuting and having an incident whilst commuting on a rush hour train. I went to meet with the Human Resources (HR) team at work and it was nice to see all my colleagues. Everyone told me how amazing I looked (this is cancer muggles for you). The hardest thing I've found about 'not looking like you have cancer', is that everyone assumes that cancer patients are bald. Maybe I used to have this preconception too. I even overheard one comment from a work colleague who said, 'her chemo can't be that bad because she hasn't lost her hair'. I had a very difficult meeting with HR, they really didn't understand, I found it incredibly awkward to have to sit in a corporate board room and attempt to articulate the reality of shitting myself on a train. So, it's about educating other people and I think whether you have to sit in a HR meeting, and bare your soul, or be very polite to the people that say, 'Oh, but you have hair'– either one is educating and it is up to us to educate other people.

By the time I finished this chemotherapy my hands and feet were ruined, the skin cracked and painful, my bowel function close to intolerable but I had to remember I was over the worst (or so I thought). I was being scanned every three months and at my next scan, I didn't even think about it potentially having spread, I guess in my head I'd had the surgery, I'd had the treatment, the tumour was gone and I just I wasn't expecting it, but, at my next oncology appointment they announced that they had found something on my liver. At first, they said they could see a lesion. 'We've found something on your liver' they said, 'It's probably nothing' – I really wish they wouldn't keep dressing it down. I had an MRI and then a PET scan. Shortly after this they decided there were lesions (plural) and that they needed to do a hepatectomy (basically a liver resection). This is an even more major a surgery than a bowel resection, it is a much riskier surgery and requires a minimum of a week in intensive care following the surgery. Your liver is divided into eight sections. I think I had sections six and seven removed (this is essentially about one third of your liver). In my mind the good thing about liver cancer, if there is a 'good' cancer to have, is that the liver is an amazing organ, you can chop as much of it out as you like and it just regenerates. Within two weeks it grows back to its original size so you can literally just keep chopping bits out.

A few months later once I had recovered from the surgery they asked me to come in to have my peripherally inserted central catheter (PICC line) installed. I made an Instagram TV (IGTV) of it being inserted, if anyone is interested. They started me on my new chemotherapy which was Oxaliplatin coupled with Capecitabine.

The first cycle was kind of all right, I just felt a bit weird. I didn't really have any side effects until the second cycle, but cycle three was bad and I had a complete meltdown. To start with they put you on a very high dose. They anticipate that with the majority of patients they will need to reduce the dosage, sometimes more than once. With me and my competitive nature I was hell bent on doing as many cycles as possible on the highest dose – in hindsight this was really stupid. I shouldn't have done cycle three on that dose, but I did. As I tried to get out of my chemotherapy chair, I collapsed. Thankfully one of the oncologist registrars happened to witness it. So, she just tapped me on the back of the shoulder and said, 'I think we'll be reducing your dose next time'. In reality it was good that the choice was taken away from me.

I am now eight months since finishing that chemotherapy. I've done over 20 hours in theatre; I've taken 4,480 pills over 48 weeks. That's 16 cycles of chemotherapy in total and I feel pretty good. I've had two clear scans and am awaiting my next one. This was meant to be my summer off cancer. I bought a horse in Portugal in the spring and I've been backwards and forwards taking part in competitions and generally making sure I am having a really fun time surrounded by amazing people. My employer told me on hearing I'd had a second clear scan that they were putting me into a redundancy process. I'm pretty pleased, in all honesty. My perspective on life has changed for the better.

My 'summer off' cancer took a bit of a sudden turn, when I started haemorrhaging (internal bleeding) very badly during a riding competition. Just as we started walking the course for my fifth round, I felt something. I looked down and, to my horror, my white jodhpurs were covered (and I mean saturated) in blood. I went in, jumped a clear round, somehow, and raced back to the stables to get my jodhpurs off. I rang my nurses and they didn't really know what to say, everyone thought I was in medical menopause – I did too, I hadn't had a period for what felt like ages. It was not a period, without wanting to gross anyone out, I was having to use two super plus sized tampons at the same time and a sanitary pad, and within 15 minutes I was bleeding out (this went on for four days).

When I returned from Portugal, my doctor referred me immediately for an ultrasound. The lady doing the ultrasound explained that your uterus lining is meant to be 14mm thick, and mine was 36mm. I then got called for a hysteroscopy a few days later. I've now had three hysteroscopies in the last two months and am waiting to hear what might be next.

So that's where I'm up to now. In conclusion I'm really grateful for my cancer. I realise that sounds odd, but I really wouldn't have the mindset that I have today if it wasn't for my illness. I wouldn't have met the people that I've met, if it wasn't for my illness. I wouldn't be doing the things I find myself doing (when I am able to), if it wasn't for my illness. Some of the most amazing opportunities have come my way this year and if it hadn't been for the illness would I have taken them, or made the most of them? Cancer has completely changed my outlook on life, for the better. I've learnt so much through hearing other people's stories along my journey and if my story can help just one other person get through theirs, then it is increasingly important to tell our stories. To be open and candid about what we go through, whilst we try and work out our new normal.

Jen

100

Cancer has affected me in many terrible, but also some positive, ways. I am very cautious of highlighting the positives too much, as I think 'non cancer' people tend to want to know about all the 'post traumatic growth', rather than hearing about the very real 'post-traumatic stress' that accompanies cancer diagnosis and treatment. Often when I say some aspect of the cancer experience was horrific, it's been met with, 'Yeah, but aren't you mostly grateful for it?' To which I just want to shake them, so they understand how horrible the whole thing is. I was not diagnosed purely to make non-cancer people feel good about life.

It has made me ill, it has taken my teeth and some of my face, it has impaired my ability to sing, to use my hands, it's taken my identity and left me with anxiety, sleep issues, pain and weakness. It's made me unable to function in the life I had before.

People are desperate for us to say we're 'all better' after treatment, whereas that is so far from reality and, in many cases, it's the bit after treatment that is the hardest part, as we struggle to navigate the post-apocalyptic wasteland that is the life we've been left with and the many permanent side effects that plague us.

People talk about a 'new normal' that you have to adjust to after cancer, and I always hated this term. I won't let cancer change me or take anything from me, if I want to change, I will be the only one to do that. So, in my fiercely determined way, I have tried to take ownership over it. I am now more in tune with my body, my needs, and what I am capable of. While I used to regularly push myself to the extreme, I am now learning to be kinder on myself. Some days I get exasperated by my inability to work a full week and then go out all weekend, sometimes I get frustrated with having to plan rest days and just do nothing. But mostly I just make sure to plan my weeks around what I know (or am learning) I'm capable of, and I am getting better at just saying 'no' to things I can't, or don't particularly want to do. Less 'should', more 'need' or 'want'.

I have made a lot of wonderful new friends and connections on the cancer circuit and am grateful for the wonderful people who have helped to carry me through my dark days, as well as the opportunities that have come out of it. The day I was diagnosed, I was welcomed into a large, supportive community of people, connected by our shared experiences. Of course this means that I now have a large group of friends who are more likely to die than your general peers, but I made a decision early on that it was worth the heartbreak of losing friends, in order to have had them in my life in the first place. My life is richer for knowing a lot of the people who are no longer here.

I have also gained an insight into and understanding of suffering. While this isn't something I would wish on anyone, it means I am a lot more compassionate and can connect with a large variety of people in their struggles. I hope I can continue to use this to help other people.

For so long the 'cancer conversation' (if you could even call it a conversation) has been mostly held by people who don't have cancer. Often by the tabloids that describe cancer as a battle, painting people who die as losers or failures, propagating the idea that those with cancer are victims who need to be pitied. Sure, we'd like some empathy and recognition that it is shit, as opposed to being dismissed with a misguided command to just 'be positive', but cancer isn't as clear cut as it used to be. We have an inherent shame around illness in our culture, that anyone who isn't perfectly well is weak (this of course leads to statistics like suicide being the biggest killer in men aged 20 to 45). This type of shame is exponentially greater when looking at Black, Asian and minority ethnic (BAME) communities, where religion is heavily involved within their culture, and cancer is either 'God's plan', or a result of someone not having prayed hard enough. But that is not my personal story to tell, and there are some brilliant people doing good work in that space.

In the days of old, people would hide away their cancer diagnosis, keep it a secret in order to avoid judgement from people who looked down on them. Even now we still seem obsessed in victim blaming – 'Oh you have cancer... so you smoked? Ate too many burnt pieces of toast, roast potatoes or red meat? Drank too much alcohol? Didn't exercise enough? No? Oh, so it must have been sugar?' So I get why it might be easier to not let people know if possible – avoid the pity, the blame and the head tilts. We are also the age of social media – of curated grids, of Instagram filters, of 'living our best lives'. When your reality doesn't match up to those you are seeing everywhere online, it can add more pressure to hide away until you're able to be back on a beach with a cocktail and flowing locks of hair (if you're lucky). But we are also slowly shifting into a world of #authenticity, where showing vulnerability is becoming more cherished, which creates a space for us with cancer to exist in the world. Hopefully not only as 'inspiration porn' (think 'look at the brave cancer warrior always being so inspirational, at least we don't have cancer, look what they've overcome'), but as a way to show other people who are struggling that they are not the only ones, and though it is shitty, it is also okay that you're not doing so well right now.

Millennials are famous for feeling like they are failing at so many aspects of life – not skinny enough, not successful enough, not rich enough. Hell, we've even coined the term 'adulting' and decided that we're not good at that either. If we keep going in that direction, we'll end up adding 'human-ing' as something we are failing at. But not if we start talking about these things, opening the conversation, realising that everyone is struggling and that is perfectly normal. With the rise of the #metoo movement we've seen how connecting, powerful and validating it can be to know that you're not the only one dealing with something. People are starting to speak out and it's time for us to do the same. And with 1 in 2 people born after 1965 destined to get cancer, we need this conversation more than ever.

It needs to come from within – those with cancer showing the way, and those without (for now, at least) listening and following suit. With 50% of people getting cancer in their lifetime, speaking about it needs to be normalised. That's about the same amount of people in the world who are born male/female, and yet we still see it being talked about in whispers and with clichés instead of facts. In the past, people would either 'get better' or 'die'. But as constant improvements are being made in the world of medicine, people are now living with cancer for many years. This negates the use of words like 'survivor', which is about as outdated as words like 'fight' and 'battle'. No one loses a battle or gets lost somewhere when they die. Cancer isn't a 'journey', it's just a shit part of life.

While I am fully aware that some people with cancer like to use these words, they are not helpful on the whole. I understand that seeing their illness as a fight gives people some sort of power over the situation, allows them to take back some of the control they feel they lost over their lives when they were handed their diagnosis. But it also puts so much pressure on people to be cured, and makes a secondary diagnosis, or any moments when things don't go according to plan, personal failures. And as long as we keep using this language, we keep propagating the myth that people can cure their own cancer by some particular level of 'fighting', and that they bring any setbacks on themselves. And, as we see when people want to know what we did to cause our cancer, the cycle keeps spiralling in the wrong direction. Even by constantly describing people as 'brave' for having cancer is damaging. Brave means 'showing no fear of dangerous or difficult things'. We need to retire this word and stop telling people with cancer they can never let on that they're scared or struggling.

Language is the most important thing we have at our disposal, let's stop using it to tell people how they should be acting and feeling and heaping shame on people for things that are entirely out of their control. I would like to strongly say that it is everyone's prerogative to do cancer in any way they want to, there should be no pressure to say certain things, or look a certain way, or even to show 'vulnerabilities' if they don't want to. But we need to work a lot harder as a society at taking the pressure off people who don't want to hide away in shame and be blamed for their own demise, in the hope that other people will then feel less pressure to stay quiet and hide.

The vast majority of my friends and community through cancer have come from social media. I wasn't big on social media before I was handed my cancer card, but as I started blogging from the day it was issued to me, people requested I set up social media accounts for it, so they would know when I had posted. Through this I have met so many wonderful people – the #cancertwitter (and Instagram) family are like none other. While I wish no one had to be part of it, since we all find ourselves in this situation, I am glad we have each other. We've taken to calling it 'the coolest club that you don't want to be a part of'.

Cancer can be so isolating (as can any chronic illness – partially due to the fact that for so long we haven't spoken about it). I have come across people in my travels who are not on social media and it shocks me every time to hear them say that even through their diagnosis and treatment, they hadn't met anyone else with the same cancer as them, or a similar age to them – 'The only person in the cancer ward for under 50's' is a line often heard. I have a super rare cancer, and even I have found people with the same diagnosis.

There is something freeing about shared experiences and just knowing that someone else knows what you are going through, at least to some extent. I find I've been able to come to terms with the whole thing a lot better than those who have only be surrounded by 'healthy' people. I've gone to events with cancer people, and for some of them, it's the first time they've been around other people with cancer, and that has been instrumental in helping them start to process their own experience.

At the beginning I joked about the idea of having 'cancer friends', I think a lot of us cringed at that thought – that we would be hanging out with people who had cancer, even perhaps after we no longer have it anymore. And of course, a lot of people I've come across I wouldn't hang out with – while we all have one thing in common, the idea that we would get along with everyone is unrealistic. But you certainly find some gems. And sometimes putting out a tweet about something that's bothering you and getting a 'me too' from people is all you need to get a bit of peace of mind that you're not going mad, losing the plot, or that there's not something very wrong with you. Part of the human condition is in fact thinking that there's something personally 'wrong' with us, so without having these conversations, those thoughts would threaten to push us further into isolation.

The internet is also giving a platform to those of us with cancer to be able to share our experiences, and I think this is starting to flow over into the media. I feel like we are at the start of a revolution. At least I hope we are, and I will do everything in my power to be a catalyst for the change we need to see.

The people I couldn't do it without

Hattie Bates

Vix Gaston

Rebecca Gwyther

Kate Kellaway

Sakis Kyratzis

Leslie Kwok

Bernard Leanse

James McNaught

Andrew Morgan

Ella Scarlett Neish

Katie Ruane

Martino Sclavi

Lucy Shaverin

Jen Taylor

Amelia Traill

Angela Traill

Piers Townley

Nell Wood

Patrons

Nick Dey

The Deptfords

Christiane Hodson

Eddie Lawson

Andrew Morton

Susanna and Tim Perutz

Simon Perutz

Sir Alan and Lady Traill

1 Philip • Oligodendroglioma (brain tumour)
2 Rebecca • Breast Cancer and Melanoma • thetwofacesofcancer.com
3 Jackie • Breast Cancer
4 Alison • Adenoid Cystic Carcinoma
5 Cindy • Breast Cancer
6 Liz • Osteoblastoma • ridingthesurvivorshiprollercoaster.wordpress.com
7 Donna • Loved one, mother
8 Georgie • Breast Cancer • lady-online.blog
9 Alejandra • Secondary Breast Cancer • honestcancermum.blogspot.com
10 Barbara • Breast Cancer with spread to lungs
11 Tasha (1986-2015) • Diffuse Intrinsic Pontine Glioma (brain tumour)
12 Becca • Triple Negative Breast Cancer • beccadancingintherain.wordpress.com
13 Sarah • Cervical Cancer • badassbaglady.com
14 Lucy (1991-2019) • Non-Hodgkin's Lymphoma
15 Nicola • Stage 4 Metastatic Bowel Cancer
16 Andrew • Acute Lymphoblastic Leukaemia • melodyberthoudblog.wordpress.com
17 Joanna • Chronic Myeloid Leukaemia (with the T315i mutation)
18 Nikki • Hodgkin's Lymphoma and Breast Cancer
19 Bridget • Breast Cancer
20 Christine • Glioneuronal Brain Tumour
21 Jane • Acute Myeloid Leukaemia
22 Laura • Secondary Incurable Breast Cancer • Instagram: baldbooblessandbeautiful
23 Nikki • Stage 3 Breast Cancer • lifeafterlola.com
24 Cristina • Stage 2 Triple Negative Breast Cancer • thecancermajlis.com
25 Charlene • Stage 4 Terminal Bowel Cancer • bowelcancerballer.wordpress.com
26 Bep • Breast Cancer • Instagram: thrivebep
27 Jolene • Stage 4 Melanoma with spread to lung, brain and bowel • melanomajo.com
28 Sylvia • Loved one, wife
29 Robert • Stage 4 Metastatic Synovial Sarcoma • Facebook: walkingwithsarcoma
30 Charlotte • Hodgkin's Lymphoma
31 Natalia • Hodgkin's Lymphoma • theclichecancerblog.com
32 Catherine • Breast Cancer • Twitter: myleftbust
33 Gillian • Breast Cancer
34 Ginny • Breast Cancer • Instagram: ginnyp360
35 Lizzie • Acute Myeloid Leukaemia
36 Angela • Polycythaemia Vera (blood cancer)
37 Grace • Pilocytic Astrocytoma (brain tumour) • almostamazinggrace.co.uk
38 Eleni • Grade 3 Triple Negative Breast Cancer • Instagram: mrswilding
39 Leanne • Uterine Cancer • Instagram: thatcstolemywomb
40 Ben • Hodgkin's Lymphoma
41 Rebecca • Stage 3 Bowel Cancer
42 Jacqui • Stage 1 Breast Cancer
43 Lucy • Metastatic Melanoma • lucysmelanomaadventure.wordpress.com
44 Victoria • Loved one, daughter
45 Nichola • Oestrogen Positive Breast Cancer • Instagram: ocdwiththebigc
46 Tracey • Thyroid Cancer and Leiomyosarcoma of the Bladder
47 Alison • Stage 3 Breast Cancer
48 Vicky • Stage 1 Triple Negative Breast Cancer • Instagram: gammy_tit
49 Mark • Stage 3 High Grade Non-Hodgkin's Lymphoma
50 Louise • Breast Cancer

Helena Traill is a London-based visual storyteller, who graduated from Central Saint Martins with a first class degree in Graphic Communication Design in 2019. Helena seeks to implement and explore the concept of narrative structure through her work, with the aim of increasing emotional engagement, offering a deeper level of communication between designer and audience.

helenatraill.co.uk